1R EUREKA!

Success in Science

Carol Chapman

Rob Musker

Daniel Nicholson

Moira Sheehan

Heinemann

Heinemann Educational Publishers
Halley Court, Jordan Hill, Oxford, OX2 8EJ
a division of Reed Educational & Professional Publishing Ltd
Heinemann is a registered trademark of Reed Educational & Professional Publishing Ltd

OXFORD MELBOURNE AUCKLAND
JOHANNESBURG BLANTYRE GABORONE
IBADAN PORTSMOUTH NH (USA) CHICAGO

© Carol Chapman, Rob Musker, Daniel Nicholson, Moira Sheehan, 2000

First published 2000

ISBN 0 435 57609 7

04 03 02 01 00
10 9 8 7 6 5 4 3 2

Edited by Ruth Holmes

Designed and typeset by Ken Vail Graphic Design, Cambridge

Original illustration © Heinemann Educational Publishers 2000

Illustrated by Barry Atkinson, Graham-Cameron Illustration (Tim Archbold, Darin Mount
and Sarah Wimperis), Nick Hawken, B.L. Kearley Ltd. (Sheila Galbreath, Jeremy Gower
and Pat Tourett), David Lock, Joseph McEwan, John Plumb, Sylvie Poggio Artists Agency
(Rhiannon Powell and Sean Victory), Linda Rogers Associates (Lorna Barnard, Keith
Howard, Gary Rees and Branwen Thomas)

Printed and bound in Spain by Edelvives

Picture research by Jennifer Johnson

Acknowledgments
The authors and publishers would like to thank the following for permission to use
copyright material: **bar chart p10**, Addison-Wesley, *Body Maintenance*; **extract p44**,
AP Watt Ltd, on behalf of The National Trust for Places of Historic Interest or Natural
Beauty; **graph p47**, *The Canadian Journal of Rural Medicine* Vol. 3, p12–19, with permission
from the Society of Rural Physicians of Canada; **map p90**, Ordnance Survey Mapping
with the permission of the Controller of Her Majesty's Stationery Office, © Crown
copyright, Licence no. 398020.

The publishers have made every effort to trace the copyright holders, but if they have
inadvertently overlooked any, they will be pleased to make the necessary arrangements
at the first opportunity.

For photograph acknowledgements, please see page 152.

Everyone can

Understand science by

Reading this book, be

Enthralled, become

Knowledgeable and

Achieve success...

...with EUREKA!

Welcome to *Eureka! Success in Science*

This is the first of three books designed to help you learn all the science ideas you need during Key Stage 3. We hope you'll enjoy the books as well as learning a lot from them.

These two pages will help you get the most out of the book so it's worth spending a couple of minutes reading them!

This book has nine units which each cover a different topic. The units have three types of pages:

Setting the scene

Each unit starts with a double-page spread which reminds you of what you know already about the topic. They tell you other interesting things, such as the place of science in everyday life and the history of some science inventions and ideas.

Learn about

► Energy

Most of the double-page spreads in a unit introduce and explain new ideas about the topic. They start with a list of these so that you can see what you are going to learn about.

Think about

► Fair tests

► Variables

Each unit has a double-page spread called Think about. You will work in pairs or small groups and discuss your answers to the questions. These pages will help you understand how scientists work and how ideas about science develop.

On the pages there are these symbols:

(a) Make a list of foods that give you a lot of energy.

Quick questions scattered through the pages help you check your knowledge and understanding of the ideas as you go along.

Questions

The questions at the end of the spread help you check you understand all the important ideas.

For your notes

These list the important ideas from the spread to help you learn, write notes and revise.

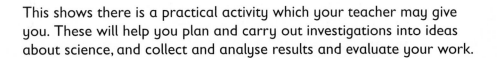

 This shows there is a practical activity which your teacher may give you. These will help you plan and carry out investigations into ideas about science, and collect and analyse results and evaluate your work.

 This shows there is an ICT activity which your teacher may give you. You will use computers to collect results from datalogging experiments, or work with spreadsheets and databases, or get useful information from CD-ROMS and the Internet.

 This shows there is a writing activity which your teacher may give you to help you write about the science you learn.

 This shows there is a discussion activity which your teacher may give you. You will share your ideas about science with others in a discussion.

At the back of the book:

 All the important scientific words in the text appear in **bold** type. They are listed with their meanings in the Glossary at the back of the book. Look there to remind yourself what they mean.

 There is an index at the very back of the book, where you can find out which pages cover a particular topic.

Activities to check your learning

Your teacher may give you these activities:

Lift-off!
When you start a unit, this short exercise reminds you what you already know about a topic.

Unit map
You can use this to think about what you already know about a topic. You can also use it to revise a topic before a test or exam.

Quiz
You can use the quiz at the end of each unit to see what you are good at and what you might need to revise.

Revision 1
You can use the revision sheets to revise a part of a unit which you aren't so good at.

End of unit test
This helps you and your teacher check what you learned during the unit, and measures your progress and success.

Contents

T	indicates Think about spread

What is energy?

Energy has something to do with food.

a Make a list of foods that give you a lot of energy.

b Jane is on a diet to lose weight. Write a list of foods she could eat for snacks.

Energy has something to do with fuels.

c How many fuels can you think of? Write down their names.

Athletes need a lot of energy to run fast or to run a long way. The more exercise we take, the more food we need. Moving has something to do with energy.

d Describe how you would feel if you had just run a long way.

e Which do you think would need more energy, running a marathon or running a 100 m sprint?

Lifting weights makes you tired and hungry. Lifting things up has something to do with energy.

f Think of six jobs that involve a lot of lifting.

g Which do you think would need more energy, lifting one brick or lifting ten bricks?

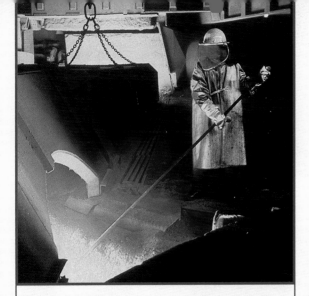

Switching off lights also saves energy. Things that give out light give out energy.

j Think of five things that give out light.

When something is hot, it is giving out energy. We save energy when we turn down our radiators.

h Make a list of things that are too hot to touch.

i How do we measure how hot something is?

We have to pay for electricity. Electricity brings energy to our homes to make things work.

k Cutting down the electricity we use saves energy as well as money. What could we do to cut down the amount of electricity we use?

When a jet plane goes very fast, you hear a booming sound. When there is a loud sound, there is a lot of energy.

l Think about supporters at a football match. What do they do to make a lot of sound?

Questions

1. Look at the pictures opposite.

   a Which things give out light?

   b Which things make sounds?

   c Which things feel hot?

   d Which pictures show things moving?

   e Which things have to be plugged in to make them work?

   f Which things would give you energy if you ate them?

   g Which pictures show things being lifted up?

2. Draw a cartoon strip about Energetic Ernie and Sluggish Sam.

What is energy?

Energy in action

Learn about

► Energy

That boy has lots of energy.

Eat your breakfast. It will give you energy.

You were very energetic today.

I haven't the energy to do that!

In science, we use the word 'energy' in a special way.

If something is moving, it has energy. A spinning skater has a lot of energy. So does a moving train, a running dog or a tree blowing about in the wind.

We call this **movement energy** or **kinetic energy**.

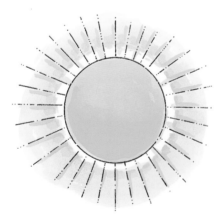

If something gives out light, it is giving out energy. The Sun is the Earth's main source of light. Most of our other sources of light are made by people.

We call this **light energy**.

If something makes sound, it is giving out energy. Some sounds come from machines like a hi-fi but a human voice or a singing bird also gives out energy. Any sound at all, whether it is loud thunder or a faint whisper, is energy.

We call this **sound energy**.

If something feels warm, it is giving out energy. The Sun warms us as well as giving us light. There are all sorts of things on the Earth that warm us. These may be natural, such as hot springs, or made by people, such as bonfires.

We call this **heat energy** or **thermal energy**.

If something is happening, then **energy** is involved.

a Make lists of things that give out:

   i light energy
   ii sound energy
   iii thermal (heat) energy.

b Choose a part of the photo and imagine you are there. What would you see and hear and feel? What would be moving?

c Describe what is happening in the photo. Try to use the words 'light energy', 'sound energy', 'thermal energy' and 'kinetic energy' as often as you can.

Questions

1. Look around the room. What things:

   a give out sound energy?
   b give out light energy?
   c show they have kinetic energy?
   d give out thermal energy?

2. Imagine you lived in the past, perhaps in a Stone Age village. What things would:

   a give out sound energy?
   b give out light energy?
   c show they have kinetic energy?
   d give out thermal energy?

3. Compare your answers to question **1** with those for question **2**. What are the differences? Why are there these differences?

For your notes

Things that move have **kinetic (movement) energy**.

Energy given out as light is called **light energy**.

Energy given out as sound is called **sound energy**.

Energy that warms is called **thermal** (heat) **energy**.

Energy on the move

Transferring energy

Energy moves from place to place. We say that energy is **transferred**.

Energy is transferred from a light bulb to our eyes.
Energy is transferred from a radio to our ears.
Energy is transferred from a heater to our skin.

a What things are used to detect:

  i a transfer of light energy?
  ii a transfer of sound energy?
  iii a transfer of thermal energy?

Energy can be carried by electricity

When we switch on a lamp, the electricity transfers the energy to the lamp. The energy leaves the lamp as light energy.

When we switch on a radio, the electricity transfers the energy to the radio. The energy leaves the radio as sound energy.

When we switch on a heater, the electricity transfers the energy to the heater. The energy leaves the heater as thermal energy.

We call energy transferred by electricity **electrical energy**.

b Look at the pictures opposite. You plug in these things (devices) to make them work. Electrical energy goes into each device. What types of energy come out of each one?

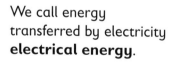
iron

radio

drill

cooker

Showing energy transfers

The energy transfer for a lamp is drawn here using arrows. The arrows show the direction of the transfer.

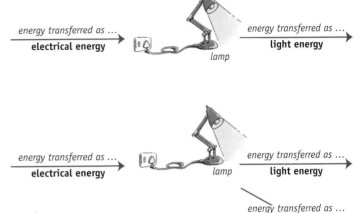

energy transferred as ...
electrical energy

energy transferred as ...
light energy

lamp

c Draw an energy transfer diagram for an electric cooker.

The energy transfer diagram for the lamp is a bit too simple, because a lamp gets hot as well. Lamps give out thermal energy as well as light energy. A side arrow shows this.

energy transferred as ...
electrical energy

energy transferred as ...
light energy

lamp

energy transferred as ...
thermal energy

d Draw an energy transfer diagram for a TV.

Measuring energy

Energy is measured in **joules**, symbol **J**. The joule was named after James Prescott Joule, a British scientist who lived between 1818 and 1889. James Joule never went to university. He started investigating energy in a small laboratory in his father's brewery. By the age of 31 he was recognised by the Royal Society as an important scientist.

James Prescott Joule.

Did you know?

One thousand joules:

● will raise the temperature of $10\,cm^3$ of water by almost 24 °C

● is the kinetic energy of a girl running at 6 metres per second

● is the energy given out by a bright light bulb in 10 seconds

● is the energy needed to play music very loud for 40 seconds

● of electrical energy costs less than $\frac{2}{1000}$ of a penny, or 0.002p.

Questions

1. A hairdryer is plugged in to make it work. When it works, the hairdryer blows hot air and makes a lot of sound. Draw an energy transfer diagram for a hairdryer.

2. Think about a washing machine. How is energy transferred to a washing machine? What types of energy does the washing machine give out? Draw an energy transfer diagram for a washing machine.

3. A dynamo can be used to make bicycle lamps work. The dynamo is turned by the bicycle wheel. The dynamo generates electricity, which goes along wires to the front and back lamps. Draw an energy transfer diagram that shows how pedalling the bike makes the lamps light.

For your notes

Energy can be moved from place to place. We say that the energy is **transferred**.

Energy transfers can be shown using energy transfer diagrams.

Energy carried by electricity is called **electrical energy**.

Stored energy

How is energy stored?

The arrow shown here has kinetic (movement) energy. Where was the energy before it was in the moving arrow?

The energy was stored in the bent bow and the stretched bowstring. The bent bow and the stretched bowstring were in tension. We call energy stored because of tension **strain energy**.

The bonfire is giving out light energy and thermal (heat) energy. Where was the energy before it was light and thermal energy?

The energy was stored in the fuel and the oxygen in the air. We call energy stored in materials **chemical energy**. Fuels, food and batteries store chemical energy.

The bucket and water in the picture have kinetic energy. Where was the energy before the water and the bucket were moving?

The energy was stored in the bucket and the water because they were lifted up. Things that are higher have energy because of gravity. We call energy stored because of gravity **gravitational energy**.

Energy can be **stored** in three ways.
It can be stored as **strain energy**, as **chemical energy** and as **gravitational energy**.

a Think of five different objects that can store energy as strain energy.

b Think of three different materials that store energy as chemical energy.

c How does a skier get gravitational energy so that she can go down the slope with lots of kinetic energy?

In and out of storage

d Look at these photos. When is the most energy stored in the trampoline? How is it stored?

e When is the most energy stored in the girl as gravitational energy?

f What happens to the energy when it is not being stored as strain energy or gravitational energy?

We can show what is happening on the trampoline using an energy transfer diagram.

| energy stored in the … |
| trampoline |
| *as **strain energy*** |

energy transferred as …
kinetic energy →

| energy stored in the … |
| girl |
| *as **gravitational energy*** |

energy transferred as …
kinetic energy →

Taking the strain in ancient times

Look at this picture of a catapult. It stored energy as strain energy so that it could give the boulder lots of kinetic energy.

g Draw an energy transfer diagram for the catapult.

h When would most strain energy be stored in the catapult?

Questions

1. How is the energy stored in **a–f**?

   a a stretched rubber band

   b a snowball at the top of a hill

   c a chocolate bar

   d a skydiver jumping out of a plane

   e a firework

   f a squashed ball

2. The stored energy is transferred from **d**, **e** and **f** above. Draw an energy transfer diagram for each.

For your notes

Energy stored because a material is being pulled or pushed is called **strain energy**.

Energy stored in fuels, food or batteries is called **chemical energy**.

Energy stored in an object because it is lifted up is called **gravitational energy**.

9

Fuel for life

Energy from food

Without food we would starve and die. Food is the fuel for our bodies. Our bodies use oxygen to release the energy stored in our food. We call the energy stored in food **chemical energy**.

We get fat if we eat too much food and take too little exercise. We get thin if we eat too little food. The amount of energy we need from food depends on what we do.

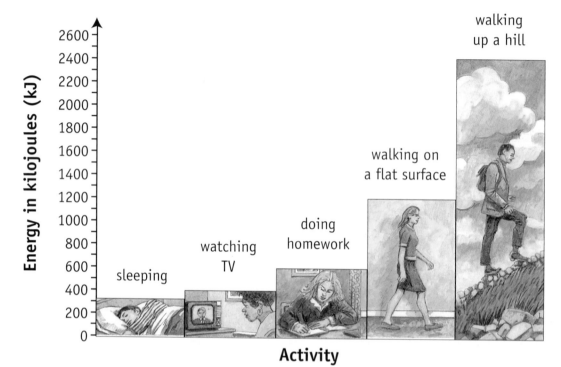

The bar chart above shows you how much energy you need to do different tasks for one hour. It shows energy measured in **kilojoules, kJ**. A kilojoule is one thousand joules.

A joule is very small. One joule is the amount of energy needed to increase the temperature of only 1 cm^3 of water by about one quarter of a degree Celsius. This means that a bath of hot water contains hundreds of millions of joules, so we use kilojoules to stop the numbers getting too big to handle.

(a) How many kilojoules do we use to sleep for one hour?

(b) How many kilojoules do we use to walk uphill for 15 minutes?

The picture opposite shows how much energy is in some different foods.

(c) How much homework can you do using the energy in one slice of bread with butter?

sausage
500 kJ

fried egg
150 kJ

chips
1000 kJ

bread and butter
600 kJ

tea with milk
65 kJ

Telling how much energy is in food

Processed foods come with a nutritional information label. This label tells us about the food. One of the things it tells us is the amount of energy in the food.

Nutritional information from a chicken and leek pie

Average values	per 100 g	per half pie
Energy	1050 kJ	1975 kJ

d How many hours could you watch TV using the energy in half a chicken and leek pie?

Unprocessed foods, like fruit, vegetables and fresh meat, do not come with a nutritional information label. You have to look up the energy content of foods like these in tables which tell you the energy for every 100 g of each food.

e Frank is on a diet. He wants to have a breakfast that uses 1500 kJ of his daily allowance. Make up a breakfast for Frank using the information in the table.

Food	Energy per 100 g	Mass of one portion
Cornflakes	1550 kJ	30 g
Milk	268 kJ	100 g (for cereal) 24 g (in coffee)
Bread	1006 kJ	35 g
Butter	2970 kJ	10 g
Marmalade	1108 kJ	15 g
Grapefruit	326 kJ	150 g

Questions

1. Use the information on these two pages to answer these questions.

   a Which contains more energy per portion, butter or marmalade?

   b Which needs more energy, walking on the flat or walking up a slope?

   c How much energy would you take in if you ate a sausage and a portion of chips?

   d How much school work could you do using the energy in the sausage and chips?

2. Imagine that you are a doctor writing for a magazine. Write an article to advise teenagers how to lose weight sensibly.

For your notes

Energy is stored in food as **chemical energy**.

Sound energy

How do we make sounds?

We make a sound when something **vibrates**. A vibration happens when something moves up and down, or from side to side. Our vocal cords, the cone inside a loudspeaker and the air in a recorder all vibrate to make sound. Look at the photograph of the steel band. The steel drums vibrate when they are struck.

How do we hear sounds?

We hear sounds with our ears. When a sound reaches our ears, the **eardrum** vibrates. This makes some small bones vibrate. The inner ear changes these vibrations into electrical signals. These electrical signals go down the **nerves** to the brain.

a Find the eardrum on the diagram. What happens to the eardrum when the sound reaches it?

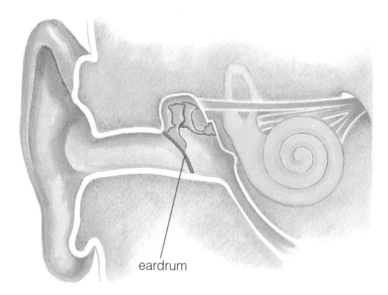

eardrum

Your ear **transfers** the energy from the sound to your brain. Look at the diagram below.

b What energy transfer happens at the eardrum?

c What energy transfer happens in the inner ear?

d How does information about the sound get to your brain?

| energy transferred as ... **sound energy** | → | *eardrum* | energy transferred as ... **kinetic energy** | → | *small bones* | energy transferred as ... **kinetic energy** | → | *inner ear* | energy transferred as .. **electrical energy** *along the nerve* |

Getting to your ear

We know that sound is made by something that vibrates.
We know that we hear sounds using our ears. How does the sound get to our ears?
The table below shows what materials sound will travel through.

Material	Will sound travel through it?
Air (Can we hear if there is only air around our ears?)	Yes
Water (Can we hear under the water?)	Yes
String (Can we hear using a string telephone?)	Yes
Wood (Can we hear sounds going through the table?)	Yes
Vacuum (Can we hear if there is nothing between us and the vibration?)	No

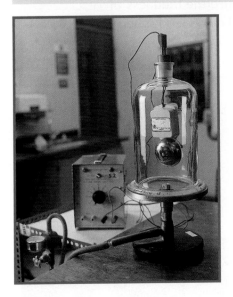

e Write a conclusion using the information in the table.

Look at the photo on the left. The air is pumped out of the jar and the sound fades away. Sound needs a material to travel through. There is nothing in a vacuum, so there is nothing for the sound to travel through. Space is nothing, so sound cannot travel through space. This is one difference between light and sound. Light can travel through space, or it would not get from the Sun to Earth.

A L I E N

In space no one can hear you scream.

Questions

Tina was inside the space centre in Florida. She was watching the space shuttle take off. There was a huge roar and the floor of the building moved under her feet. A man next to her suggested that space shuttles would be taking off from the Moon in ten years' time.

1. What was making the sound?

2. How did the roar reach Tina's ears?

3. What happened in Tina's ears when the sound reached them?

4. Why did the floor move under Tina's feet?

Imagine being on a space centre on the Moon watching a space shuttle take off. There would be no roar but the floor would move.

5. Why would there be no roar?

6. Why would the floor move?

For your notes

Sound is made by **vibrations**.

The **eardrum** vibrates when sound enters the ear.

Sound needs a material to travel though. It cannot travel through a vacuum.

More energy, more sound?

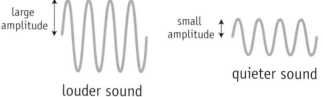
Making a sound louder

The loudness of a sound depends on how big the vibrations are. Big vibrations give loud sounds. Small vibrations give quiet sounds. A **cathode ray oscilloscope** (**CRO** for short) lets us see the vibrations.

The **amplitude** tells us how big the vibrations are. The larger the amplitude, the louder the sound.

large amplitude ↕

louder sound

small amplitude ↕

quieter sound

Loud sounds have more energy

The louder a sound is, the more energy it has. This means that a loud sound can transfer more energy than a quiet sound. We measure the loudness of sounds in **decibels**, **dB**. A very quiet whisper might be 1 dB. A loud sound, like a vacuum cleaner, is 70 dB. A jet plane overhead is about 100 dB.

A sound of more than 120 dB hurts. It transfers too much energy to our ears. An extremely loud sound like this can damage the eardrum.

Sounds of more than about 90–100 dB will not damage the eardrum but they can be dangerous if they go on for a long time. Long-term exposure to loud sounds damages the nerve that links the inner ear to the brain. People with noisy jobs wear ear protectors to stop them losing their hearing.

ⓐ The music in some clubs is played at about 110 dB. People working in the club are at a high risk of damaging their hearing, but the people who visit the club are in less danger. Why?

Changing the pitch of a sound

The **pitch** of a sound is how high or low it is. Quick vibrations give high-pitched sounds. Slow vibrations give low-pitched sounds. Again, we can see this on a CRO.

The **frequency** tells us how quick the vibrations are. The higher the frequency, the higher the pitch of the sound. Frequency is measured in **hertz, Hz** or **kilohertz, kHz**. There are 1000 Hz in 1 kHz.

b Jane hears:
  i a very quiet, low-pitched sound
  ii a louder, higher-pitched sound.

Draw what each sound might look like on a CRO.

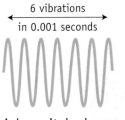

6 vibrations
in 0.001 seconds

higher-pitched sound

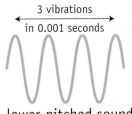

3 vibrations
in 0.001 seconds

lower-pitched sound

Hearing the sound

Some people can hear more sounds than others. Different animals hear different frequencies. Look at the diagram at the side of the page.

c Suggest a frequency that young people can hear but older people have difficulty hearing.

d Imagine you are designing a mobile telephone system. The wider the range of frequency the telephone transmits, the more expensive it will be to build. What range of frequencies would you design for?

Frequency
in kilohertz (kHz)

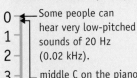

0 — Some people can hear very low-pitched sounds of 20 Hz (0.02 kHz).
1
2
3 — middle C on the piano
4 — A piccolo can play the C four octaves above middle C.
5
6 — The 'th' sound, like in 'thing', is a high-pitched sound of 6 kHz.
7
8
9
10
11
12 — Elephants hear up to only 12 kHz.
13
14
15 — Many older humans cannot hear high-pitched sounds above 15 kHz.
16
17
18
19
20 — Some humans (young ones!) can hear very high-pitched sounds, up to 20 kHz.

Cats can hear up to 32 kHz.

Dogs can hear up to 46 kHz.

Dolphins can hear up to 100 kHz.

Bats can hear up to 150 kHz.

Questions

1. Pair up the words below, then write two sentences. Each sentence should contain one pair of words.

> amplitude   frequency
> pitch   loudness

2. There are laws about how much noise there can be in the workplace. Employers who break these laws may have to pay compensation.

  a Explain what might happen to someone who works in a noisy factory.

  b Imagine that an employer had provided ear protectors but the employee had not worn them. Should compensation be paid?

For your notes

Loud sounds transfer a lot of energy. Loud sounds can damage your hearing.

The larger the **amplitude** of a vibration, the louder the sound.

The larger the **frequency** of a vibration, the higher the **pitch** of the sound.

Some people can hear higher-pitched sounds than others.

Energy trails

Tracking the energy

Energy can be moved about. Energy can be stored. However, it is impossible to make or destroy energy. We say that energy is **conserved**.

The people above are talking about the energy in a banana. We can show this using an energy transfer diagram.

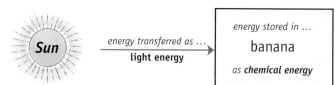

Sun → *energy transferred as ...* **light energy** → *energy stored in ...* banana *as chemical energy*

Look at the picture above. Again, we can show an energy transfer diagram for the cloud.

Sun → *energy transferred as ...* **thermal energy** → *energy stored in ...* water in cloud *as gravitational energy*

16

a An athlete lifts some weights. The energy stored as gravitational energy in the weights came from the Sun. On the way, it was stored as chemical energy in food, and as chemical energy in the athlete (maybe in fat). Use the plan below to draw an energy transfer diagram.

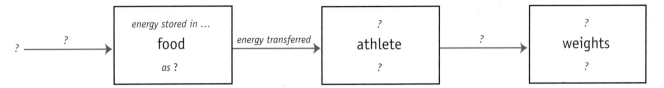

Not all the energy is useful to us

When the athlete lifts the weights, he gets hot. Not all the energy is used to lift up the weights. Some is transferred as thermal energy instead. We show this as a side arrow.

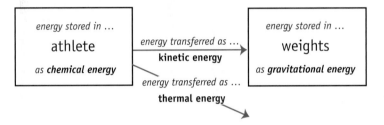

When you burn a fuel, you want the thermal energy it can release. However, it also gives out light energy, which you do not really want.

b Draw an energy transfer diagram for burning wood. Show the useful energy transfers and the unwanted energy transfers.

Think about a car. Cars use petrol or diesel for fuel. Petrol and diesel are made from crude oil. Crude oil is made from dead bodies of tiny animals that lived in the sea. These animals would have eaten tiny plants as food.

c Draw an energy transfer diagram for a car, ending up with the kinetic energy of the car and starting with the Sun. Add in any wasted energy as side arrows.

Questions

1. Energy is stored in:

   a a pat of butter   **b** a jet plane up in the air   **c** a drawn bow.

   Draw energy transfer diagrams to show how energy from the Sun ended up stored in each.

2. Think about a TV. Draw an energy transfer diagram for a TV, showing both useful and unwanted energy transfers.

3. A cyclist is at the top of a hill. She freewheels down the hill, using her brakes so she does not go too fast. The brakes rub on the wheels. They heat up as the bike slows down. Draw an energy transfer diagram. Try to include all the energy transfers.

For your notes

Energy is **conserved**. It is impossible to create or destroy energy.

Most energy can be tracked back to the Sun.

When energy is transferred, only some of it can be used.

The best fuel?

Investigating fuels

A class investigated the energy given out by two different fuels, lighter fuel and firelighters. They burned the fuels and heated water with them. The fuel that heated up the water more gave out the more energy.

The class tested each fuel in turn.

a They decided to use the same mass of each fuel. Why do you think they did this?

b They decided to heat the same volume of water with each fuel. Why do you think they did this?

The pictures below show Shaibal and Pippa's experiment with lighter fuel.

1. They used 100 cm³ of water and 2 g of fuel.

2. They took the temperature of the water at the start and found it was 21 °C.

3. They took the temperature when all the fuel had burned away and found that it was 46 °C.

4. They took the start temperature away from the end temperature to find out how much the fuel had heated the water:

$$\begin{array}{r} 46 \\ -\ 21 \\ \hline 25\,°C \end{array}$$

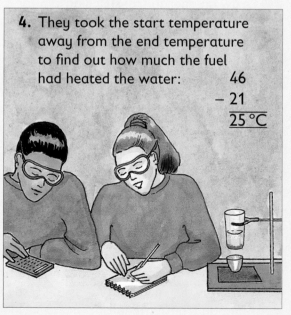

Each group then did another experiment using firelighters instead of lighter fuel. They wanted to compare the firelighters with the lighter fuel.

Shaibal and Pippa burned 5 g of firelighter and heated 100 cm³ of water. The temperature of the water was 21 °C at the start and 82 °C at the end.

c By how much did the fuel heat the water?

d Do you think this was a fair test? Explain your answer.

e Would you have done the experiment in the same way as Shaibal and Pippa? Explain your answer.

Variables

These three things could be different at the start of this investigation. They are **variables**. They are:

● the type of fuel   ● the mass of fuel   ● the volume of water.

We are investigating the type of fuel, so this is the only one we change. It is called the **input variable**.

The change in water temperature depends on the type of fuel being used. This is called the **outcome variable**. This is the variable that we measure.

Lighter fuel again

Shaibal and Pippa then did a different investigation. They used lighter fuel this time. The table shows their results.

Mass of fuel in g	Amount of water in cm³	Temperature of water at start in °C	Temperature of water at end in °C	Temperature rise in °C
1.0	100	21	33	12
1.5	100	21	38	17
2.0	100	21	46	25
2.5	100	21	52	31
3.0	100	21	59	38

f What was the input variable for this investigation?

g What was the outcome variable?

h What variables did Shaibal and Pippa keep the same to make it a fair test?

i Make a line graph of Shaibal and Pippa's results. Put the input variable along the bottom and the outcome variable up the side. Draw the best straight line you can through the points.

We use the word **relationship** to describe how the outcome variable changes when the input variable is changed.

The temperature rises less as you burn a bigger mass of fuel.

There is no relationship between the rise in temperature and the mass of fuel you burn.

The temperature rises more as you burn a bigger mass of fuel.

j Is there a relationship between the temperature rise (the outcome variable) and the mass of fuel (the input variable)? If so, describe it.

19

The birthday party

Cake and ice lollies

Sarah was helping prepare her little brother Matthew's birthday party. First she made chocolate icing for the birthday cake. She warmed pieces of chocolate in a bowl. Sarah could see the chocolate slowly becoming softer. She stirred it as it became runny. Once the chocolate was nice and runny Dad poured it on top of the cake. To begin with, the icing dripped a bit. Dad said it would be fine if they left it to cool.

a What do you think will happen to the chocolate as it cools down?

As it was summer, Matthew and his friends were going to play outside. Mum said they would get hot. Sarah decided to make them some ice lollies. She poured some orange squash into a jug of water and stirred it to mix it well. Then she poured the mixture into the lolly moulds and put them into the freezer. She kept checking to see when they were ready. Gradually ice started to form on top. It took several hours before they were ready.

b What was happening when the lolly mixture was put in the freezer?

Balloons and bubbles

There was still plenty of time before the party. Matthew was getting very excited so Dad played with him while Sarah helped Mum with the decorations. They blew up lots of coloured balloons and tied strings on to them. They hung them round the walls. Sarah noticed how the balloons hung down. Dad had bought Matthew a special one. It was filled with a gas called helium and it floated up to the ceiling and stayed there.

'Blowing up balloons is thirsty work,' puffed Sarah. She poured them all a glass of lemonade. Sarah sat and watched the bubbles on the inside of her glass. Every now and then a bubble would float up to the top and vanish. 'I wonder why bubbles go up but not down,' she thought.

c Why did the helium balloon float to the ceiling?

d Why do you think the bubbles went up but not down?

Ice cream and candles

Matthew's friends came and he had lots of presents. Everyone sang 'Happy Birthday' as Mum came in with the cake. Sarah could see how the tops of the candles were melting and the wax was running down.

They had ice cream after they'd eaten the cake. Dad got the ice cream out of the freezer. It was much too hard to get out of the tub. They had to leave it for a few minutes.

e What was happening to the candle wax?

f What happened to the ice cream when they left it for a few minutes?

All change

After the party, Sarah had a bath. As she lay there, she watched the steam coming off the bath and turning into droplets on the bathroom window. Sarah thought about all the changes she had seen today: solids turning into liquids, liquids into solids, gases into liquids. She wondered what it would be like if everything stayed the same all the time. She thought about the chocolate icing, and lollies and ice cream. 'I'm glad things do change,' she decided.

Questions

1. Make a table of all the solids, liquids and gases that Sarah found out about.

2. a Name five solids that you can find in a laboratory.

  b Name two liquids that you can find there.

  c Name two gases that you can find there.

3. Write a story about a day out at the beach. Describe all the solids, liquids and gases that you see there.

Different properties

Everything we can pick up or touch is made of **matter**. Solids, liquids and gases are three kinds of matter. They behave in very different ways. A solid is different from a liquid, and they are both very different from a gas. They have different **properties**.

Solids

The saucepan in the photo is an example of a **solid**.

Solids are usually hard – they cannot be squashed easily. The shape of the saucepan is the same wherever you put it. We say that a solid has a fixed shape. Also, the saucepan will have the same volume everywhere. A solid has a fixed volume.

Most solids are very difficult to pour. You cannot usually put a spoon into a solid and give it a stir. You can pour and stir solids that are powders or small crystals, like salt.

The silo in the photo is full of grain. To move the grain, air is blown in to push the particles apart. This makes the grain behave like a liquid. It flows down the pipe.

Quicksand can be very dangerous. It is a mixture of water and sand. The water gets in between the grains of sand and allows them to move. The sand behaves like a liquid and cannot support your weight. You will sink into it.

Liquids

The drink in the photo is an example of a **liquid**.

Liquids are not hard like solids. They can be poured from one container to another. Some liquids, such as water, are very runny and can flow very quickly. Other liquids, such as oil, are much thicker and will flow much more slowly. Liquids can be stirred, but some are easier to stir than others.

The drink in the photo has the same shape as the glass it is in. It is tall and thin. Before it came out of the bottle it was bottle-shaped. The shape of a liquid changes to fit the bottom of the container it is in.

Like solids, liquids cannot be squashed, as the person in the cartoon is about to find out!

The volume of a liquid will stay the same in any container. One litre of drink will fit into lots of different shaped containers, but there will always be one litre.

Gases

The air inside the balloons above is an example of a **gas**.

Gases are not hard like solids. They can flow from one place to another like liquids do, but gases move even quicker than liquids. Wind is air flowing from one place to another.

The shape and volume of a gas does not stay the same. It changes to fill up all of the container. The gas inside a balloon is balloon-shaped. It is very easy to squash a balloon. All gases can be squashed easily.

Questions

1. Copy and complete these sentences.
   Everything in the world is made of _____.
   Solids, liquids and gases are the three kinds of _____.

2. Copy the table and complete it by putting either a tick (✓) or a cross (✗) in each box.

Property	Solid	Liquid	Gas
Easy to pour	✗	✓	✓
Easy to squash			
Fixed shape			
Fixed volume			

3. The first bicycle tyres were solid. Explain why today's air-filled tyres give a more comfortable ride than solid tyres.

4. What three properties do solids have that make them useful building materials?

For your notes

Solids are hard and have a fixed shape and fixed volume.

Liquids have a fixed volume. They are runny and can be poured.

Gases do not have a fixed shape or a fixed volume. They take the shape of their container. They can be squashed easily.

Particle power

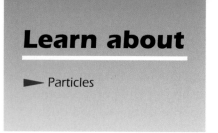

A closer look

You have already seen that solids, liquids and gases behave in different ways. Why is a solid hard? Why is a liquid runny? To find out, let's take a closer look at them.

Scientists believe that everything is made of tiny **particles**. These particles are arranged in different ways in solids, liquids and gases. This idea is called the **particle model**.

Solids

In a solid, the particles are very close together and they are held together by strong forces of attraction. The particles have a regular pattern. They cannot move about very much.

Solids cannot be squashed easily because the particles are already very close. It difficult to get them any closer. This also explains why the shape of the solid does not change and its volume stays the same.

Solids cannot be poured or stirred because the particles are joined together very strongly.

a Explain why it is difficult to squash a solid.

Liquids

In a liquid, the particles are almost as close together as they are in a solid. They are close enough to make it difficult to squash the liquid.

The particles in a liquid are still held together, but not as strongly as in a solid. They are not arranged in a regular pattern, but in a more random way. The particles can slide over each other and they keep changing position. This is why the shape of a liquid changes to fill the bottom of its container. Because the particles can move around, a liquid is easy to pour and stir.

b Explain why it is easy to pour a liquid.

Gases

In a gas, the particles are very far apart. Most of a gas is empty space. The gas can be squashed easily because there is space between the particles. They can be moved closer together. The particles are not attached to each other at all.

The particles of a gas are not in a regular pattern, they are arranged at random. They are always moving around and changing their position. Because they are always moving, they fill all of their container. The shape and volume of the gas changes to match the container they are in.

c Explain why gases can flow.

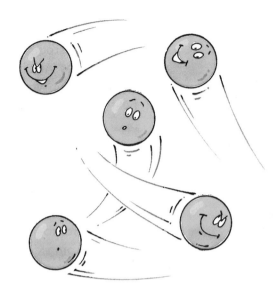

Density

The cube in this picture has lots of particles packed into a small volume. This makes it heavy. The cube is **dense**. Most solids are dense. Many liquids are also dense.

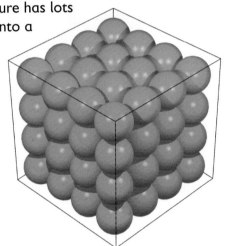

The cube in this picture has only a few particles and they are very spread out. This makes it lighter than the other cube. It is less dense. Gases are not very dense.

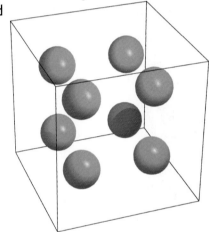

Questions

1. Copy and complete these sentences.
   Solids have a fixed shape because their particles …
   Gases fill all of their container because their particles …
   Liquids are hard to squash because their particles …

2. One litre of water produces 1333 litres of steam. Explain why there is such a big increase in volume.

3. What makes solids denser than gases?

4. Which would you rather carry through an obstacle course, a bottle containing 1 kg of water or a balloon containing 1 kg of air? Explain your answer carefully.

For your notes

Everything is made of **particles**.

In a solid, the particles are very close and in a neat pattern.

In a liquid, the particles are slightly further apart and have a less regular pattern.

In a gas, the particles are far apart and have no pattern at all.

Solids and liquids are more **dense** than gases.

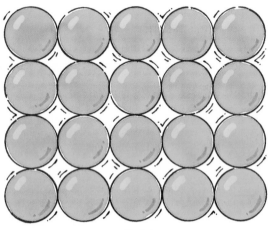

Learn about

► Melting, evaporating and freezing

How particles move

Particles do not stay still. They are always moving. Particles in solids, liquids and gases move in a different ways. The more energy they have, the faster they move.

Melting and freezing

In a solid, the particles are joined together and are very close to each other. The particles cannot move very far. They just jiggle quickly from side to side. We say that they are **vibrating**.

In a liquid, the particles are not lined up in rows, so they take up a bit more space. They are not joined very tightly. The particles in a liquid can move about more than the particles in a solid. They can slide over each other.

If you heat a solid, the particles start to vibrate faster. The hotter it gets, the faster the particles move. Eventually they vibrate so quickly that they are not joined so tightly and they move away from each other a little. When this happens, the solid turns into a liquid. We say that the solid is **melting**.

The opposite of this is **freezing**. The particles slow down as they get colder. They get closer together and form a solid.

Solid

Liquid

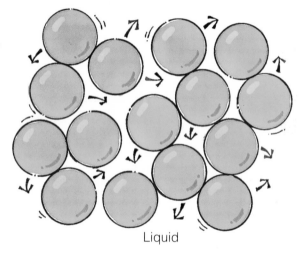

Gas

Evaporating and condensing

In a gas, the particles are very far apart from each other. They are constantly moving around all over the place.

When you heat a liquid, the particles move faster. Eventually they move so much that some of them break away from the other particles and move around on their own. When this happens, some of the liquid turns into a gas. We say the liquid is **evaporating**.

The opposite of this is **condensing**. The particles slow down as they lose thermal energy. They get closer together and form a liquid.

Changes of state

These changes from solid to liquid or liquid to gas and back again are called **changes of state**. Solids, liquids and gases are the **three states of matter**.

solid  melting / freezing   liquid 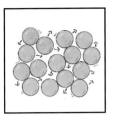 evaporating / condensing   gas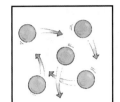

The Snowman

On cold days when it snows
I build a snowman
with a carroty nose

My snowman shrinks
when the sun is around
leaving puddles on the ground

a What change of state is illustrated in the poem?

b How is it illustrated?

c What would happen to the puddles if it got warmer?

Questions

1. Copy and complete these sentences.
   When you heat particles, they move …
   When you cool particles, they move …

2. Describe the differences in the way that particles move in a solid, a liquid and a gas.

3. Write your own poem, like The Snowman, about the changes of state of a tray of water put in the freezer overnight and then left out in a sunny spot.

For your notes

Particles move faster when they are heated. They slow down when they are cooled.

A solid melts because the particles move away from each other.

A liquid evaporates because the particles move around on their own.

These changes are called **changes of state**.

27

Where does it go?

When you add sugar to a cup of tea, the sugar seems to disappear. You know it is still there because you can taste it. The sugar hasn't vanished, it has **dissolved**.

The picture below shows what happens to the particles when sugar dissolves in water.

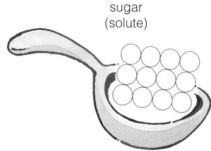

sugar
(solute)

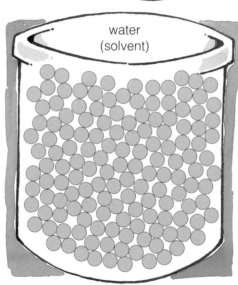

water
(solvent)

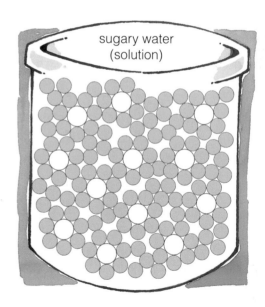

sugary water
(solution)

The particles in the sugar break apart and mix with the water particles. You cannot see the particles because they are spread throughout the liquid. This is called a sugar **solution**.

The substance that dissolves is called the **solute**. The liquid that it dissolves in is called the **solvent**. The mixture of solute dissolved in solvent is called a **solution**.

If you keep adding sugar to the water, eventually it will start to sink to the bottom rather than dissolving. No more sugar can dissolve. We say that the solution is **saturated**.

Speed it up

To make the sugar dissolve faster, you can do the following:

- Use hotter water. The particles move around more and so get mixed up faster.
- Stir it. The particles move around more, helping to mix up the sugar and the water.
- Use finer sugar. If you use a sugar cube, the particles on the outside will dissolve first. Particles in the middle of the cube will stay dry for quite a while. If you crush the cube up, then a lot more of the sugar is getting wet.

> **Did you know?**
>
> Sugar and salt will not dissolve in petrol.

Different solvents

Some substances, such as nail varnish, do not dissolve in water. Nail varnish is **insoluble** in water. If you want to remove nail varnish then you have to use a liquid called acetone. This is another type of solvent. The nail varnish is **soluble** in acetone.

Some felt-tip pens are filled with waterproof ink. You can use them to label beakers or test tubes. The ink is insoluble in water, so it does not dissolve when it gets wet. To remove the ink you have to use alcohol, another solvent. The ink is soluble in alcohol.

Dry cleaning

Some clothes have to be dry-cleaned. The clothes are sprayed with a special solvent that dissolves grease and dirt. The solvent then evaporates, leaving the clothes clean. This is useful for cleaning fabrics that would be damaged by soaking them in water and detergent.

Questions

1. Copy and complete these sentences.
   If you stir salt into water, it will _____. The salt is called the _____ and the water is called the _____. The mixture of salt and water is called a _____.

2. Joanna put a sugar lump into a cup of cold water and left it to stand. It took a long time to dissolve. Suggest three ways of making the sugar dissolve quicker.

3. Hot water will dissolve more sugar than cold water. Use your knowledge of particles to explain why this is.

> **For your notes**
>
> A **solute** is a substance that **dissolves** in a liquid called a **solvent**. The particles in the solute break apart and mix with the particles in the solvent.
>
> The mixture of solute dissolved in solvent is called a **solution**.
>
> Different solutes dissolve in different solvents.

Getting drinking water

Imagine that you are on a desert island. There is no fresh water for you to drink, only sea water. Sea water is a solution of salt in water. It is not good to drink. How could you separate the water and the salt to get drinking water?

If you boiled the water, it would turn into a gas. The salt would be left behind. To get drinking water, we can use a process called **distillation**. This is shown in the diagram below.

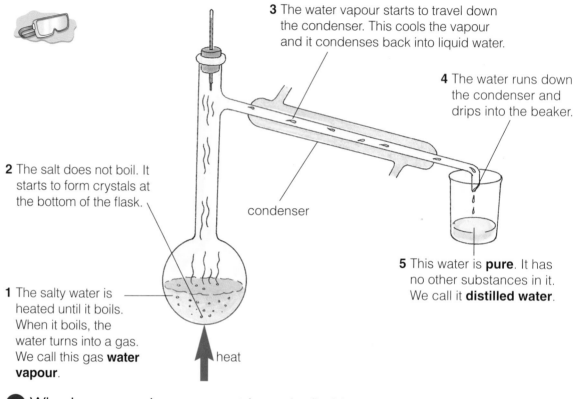

3 The water vapour starts to travel down the condenser. This cools the vapour and it condenses back into liquid water.

4 The water runs down the condenser and drips into the beaker.

2 The salt does not boil. It starts to form crystals at the bottom of the flask.

condenser

1 The salty water is heated until it boils. When it boils, the water turns into a gas. We call this gas **water vapour**.

heat

5 This water is **pure**. It has no other substances in it. We call it **distilled water**.

ⓐ What happens to the water particles in the flask?

ⓑ What happens to the water particles in the condenser?

Pure water

The distilled water is **pure**. It only has one substance in it.

If you boil pure water, all the water will turn to water vapour. Nothing will be left behind in the flask.

Water that contains another substance, such as salt or chalk, is not pure. If you boil this water, the salt or chalk will be left behind.

Large-scale distillation

The photo shows a desalination plant. These are used in some countries to turn sea water into drinking water. They are quite expensive to run, because they need a lot of energy.

Separating inks

The ink in your pen is probably not made of one colour. It is a **mixture** of colours or dyes. To separate them out, we can use a method called **chromatography**.

Different inks are put along the edge of a piece of filter paper. This is dipped into a solvent, such as water. As the solvent moves up the paper, the particles of dye are carried up with it.

How far each dye moves depends on how soluble it is. Substances that are very soluble move a long way up the paper. Substances that are not very soluble only move a short distance up the paper.

Look at the picture below.

c Which one of these inks is a mixture?

d How many different dyes was it made of?

e What can you say about how soluble each dye is?

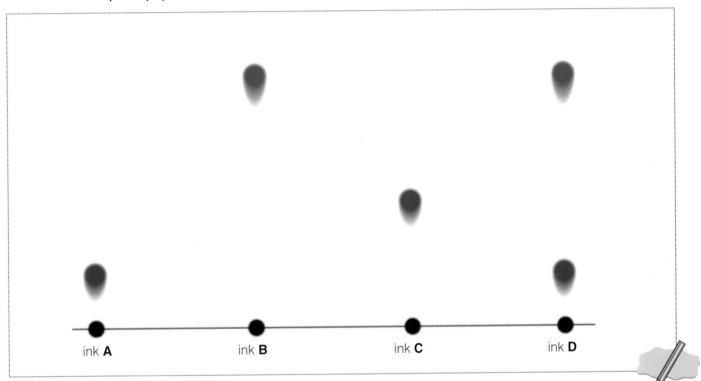

ink **A**   ink **B**   ink **C**   ink **D**

Questions

1. Copy and complete these sentences.
To separate salt and water, we can use a method called
_____. The water is boiled and turns into a
_____. The water _____ reaches the
condenser where it cools down and _____. This
pure water is called _____ water.

2. Is the ink in your pen a mixture? Plan an experiment to find out.

3. Distilled water is often used in steam irons. Why do you think this is? What happens if tap water is used?

For your notes

Distillation can be used to separate a pure liquid from a solution.

Chromatography is a way of separating a mixture of dyes.

31

Crime and colours

Finding Mr X

Shaheen is a forensic scientist. It is her job to help the police solve crimes. She uses different methods to examine clues. It is important that she analyses the results of her investigations very carefully.

Mr Jones's garden gnome Bob has been kidnapped. A ransom note from the kidnapper was signed 'Mr X' in blue felt-tip pen.

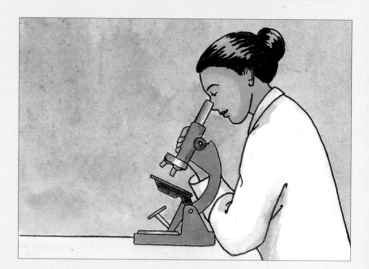

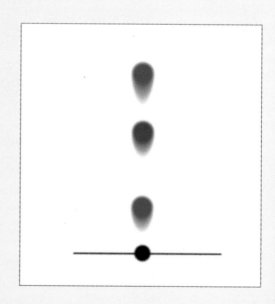

I have Bob the gnome, and I want £100

Mr X

Mr Jones suspects that one of his neighbours has kidnapped Bob. The police found a blue felt-tip pen in four of his neighbours' houses.

They need to prove that one of these pens was the one used to write the ransom note. Using chromatography, Shaheen separated the ink on the ransom note into its different dyes.

Here is the **chromatogram** that she made.

a How many different dyes do you think are in the blue ink?

b Which dye is the most soluble in the solvent Shaheen used? Explain your answer.

Shaheen then did the same thing for each of the neighbours' pens. She compared these with the ransom note. Her results are shown on the next page.

c Which pen do you think was used to write the ransom note? Explain your answer.

d Give three reasons why this is not enough to prove without doubt who the kidnapper is.

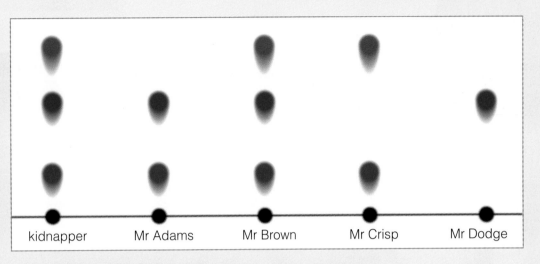

kidnapper   Mr Adams   Mr Brown   Mr Crisp   Mr Dodge

Analysing foods

Many foods have artificial colours added to make the colours brighter. Chromatography can also be used to look at these colourings.

The Pluto Sweetie firm brought out a new range of orange and yellow sweets called Brighties. Tony was worried that the sweets might contain a food colouring called sunburst yellow. He is allergic to sunburst yellow – it brings him out in big red spots. He is not allergic to other yellow colours.

Tony used chromatography to separate out the colours in the orange and yellow sweets. He compared these with four different yellow food colours.

Questions

Look at Tony's chromatogram opposite and discuss the questions with your partner to help him analyse his results.

1. What colours are in an orange Brightie?

2. What colours are in a yellow Brightie?

3. What colour was not found in either of the sweets?

4. Will orange Brighties make Tony ill? Explain your answer.

5. Will yellow Brighties make Tony ill? Explain your answer.

6. What do food companies normally do to help people find out what additives are in their foods?

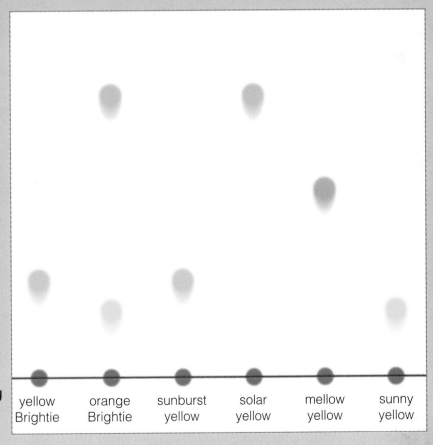

yellow Brightie   orange Brightie   sunburst yellow   solar yellow   mellow yellow   sunny yellow

Lookalikes

Human robots?

A new television programme called Quasar Quest 5 has robots that look exactly like humans. They walk and even talk like humans.

Zac235 is a robot and he assists Mr Zachariah. They look identical.

ALL LIVING THINGS
- MOVE
- RESPIRE
- SENSE CHANGES
- GROW
- REPRODUCE
- FEED
- EXCRETE WASTE

Looking after the crew

Arrangements are made on the Quasar ship for the human crew members to carry out the life processes.

- There is enough space for **M**ovement.

- Cylinders under the deck give out oxygen. The crew use this for **R**espiration, getting energy from food.

- Regular hearing and sight tests check out **S**ensitivity.

- Clothing is made from super stretch fabrics that stretch with **G**rowth.

- **R**eproduction will happen, babies will be born, so the nursery is specially equipped for the infants.

- The toilets recycle waste water from **E**xcretion for drinking and washing.

- **N**utrition is important, but all food has to be powdered to save space.

Mrs Gren is the flight attendant in charge of remembering all of this. You can use the letters in her name to help you to remember the life processes.

Did you know?

- On 17 December 1994, Pipin Ferreras dived underwater to a depth of 127 m with a single breath of air. He was under the water for 2 minutes 28 seconds!

- Human urine is 95% water.

- A dormouse goes to sleep in the autumn and wakes up in the spring with an enormous appetite!

Fact files

Read the fact files about
Mr Zachariah and Zac235.
The files give information
about the things they can do.

Did you know?

Humans have the most
complex brain of all animals.
They have the power to think
before they act. A robot has
to be programmed to react
to changes.

FACT FILE: Mr Zachariah

Movement: can walk at a speed of 3 km/hour

Breathing: breathes air

Sensors: responds to sound, light, temperature changes, chemicals and touch

Growth: stopped at a final height of 2 metres

Family: is the father of two children

Diet: includes chicken, fish, vegetables and fruit

Special requests: needs to have a toilet on board

FACT FILE: Zac235

Movement: can walk at a speed of 3 km/hour

Breathing: not necessary

Sensors: responds to sound, light, temperature changes, chemicals and touch

Growth: fixed size

Family: is not possible

Diet: nuclear fuel cells

Special requests: oil change

Did you know?

A French woman called Jeanne
Calment was 121 years old
in 1996.

Did you know?

A human can survive as long as
60 days without food, but less
than 60 hours without water.

Questions

1. Some non-living things carry out
   some (but not all) of the life
   processes.

   a What life processes do both
      Mr Zachariah and Zac235 do?

   b What can Mr Zachariah do
      that Zac235 cannot do?

   c What can Zac235 do that
      Mr Zachariah cannot do?

2. Quest 5 is a mission into space that will take 110 years.
   Suggest three reasons why it is important to have both
   robots and humans on board.

3. Imagine that Zac235 and the other robots are planning to
   take over the Universe. Zac is posing as Mr Zachariah.
   Suggest three ways of proving that he is an imposter.

4. The crew of Quasar Quest 5 have found some green slime
   on one of Jupiter's moons. How can they test
   it to find out whether it is living or non-living?

Sorting out living things

Living things

We can group everything on Earth as either living or non-living. We call living things **organisms**. The smallest living things are called **microorganisms** and you need a microscope to study them. **Bacteria** and **viruses** are microorganisms. There are lots of different kinds of organisms so we put them in groups to make them easier to study.

a How do we decide whether something is living or non-living?

Classifying organisms

To put organisms into groups, we look at them and see what special parts they have or what things they do. These are called their **features**. We put organisms that have similar features into the same group. This grouping is called **classification**. The table shows how we start to classify living things.

Learn about

► Classification

Animals	Plants	Microorganisms	Fungi
Human	Lime tree	**Virus**	Toadstool
Horse			
	Primrose	**Bacterium**	**Mould**
Spider			
Feed on other animals or plants	Make their own food	**Can only be seen with a microscope**	Feed on rotting material
Most move around	Green		

Wherever you look, you will find examples of all these groups of organisms. You will find animals, plants, microorganisms and fungi in soil or in a pond. There are many different living things even in very cold places like the Arctic.

Did you know?

The first scientist to classify animals was a Frenchman called Georges Cuvier who lived in the eighteenth century. He collected bones and shells and studied them carefully. He was particularly interested in elephants. He described the exact size and measurements of an extinct type of elephant from one tooth fossil!

b How do you think Cuvier described an elephant from its tooth? What measurements would he have compared?

Animal X-rays

All the animals are put into two groups, those with a backbone and those without a backbone.

Cuvier grouped all the animals with backbones together and called them Vertebrata, a Latin word for jointed backbone. In classification today, we call animals with backbones **vertebrates**. We call animals without backbones **invertebrates**.

Here are some animal X-rays from the Arctic.

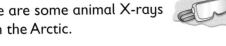

c Classify each animal as a vertebrate or an invertebrate.

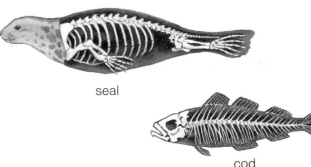
seal

starfish

cod

octopus

crab

arctic tern

Questions

1. Explain how living things are classified.

2. How are plants different from animals?

3. Fungi look a bit like plants. Why are fungi in a group of their own?

4. Which of these animals are vertebrates?

> earthworm   octopus   robin   toad   rat
> snake   centipede   bat   squirrel

5. *Challenge:* design a key to classify vertebrates and invertebrates.

For your notes

We can sort living things into groups with similar **features**. This is called **classification**.

Vertebrates are animals with a backbone.

Invertebrates are animals without a backbone.

More animal groups

Five groups of vertebrates

The vertebrates are divided into five smaller groups.

Mammals	Birds	Reptiles	Amphibians	Fish
Lion	Eagle	Crocodile	Frog	Shark

Sort yourself out

The human body has a backbone, so we are **vertebrates**. Along with the lions, apes, dogs, cats and many other furry animals, we are classified as **mammals**.

Mammals

These are the features of mammals:

- Their babies develop inside the mother's body.
- The mother feeds the young on milk, which she makes in her **mammary glands**.
- They have hairy skin to insulate them. They are warm blooded. This means they keep their body temperature constant at 37 °C.

The rest of the vertebrates apart from mammals are classified as:

- birds
- reptiles
- amphibians
- fish.

Did you know?

Mammals, birds, reptiles and amphibians breathe air using lungs.

Did you know?

Mammals and birds are the only groups of vertebrates that look after their young. Reptiles, amphibians and fish usually leave their young to fend for themselves.

Birds

These are the features of **birds**:

- They lay eggs with a hard shell.
- They look after their young after they have hatched.
- They have feathers and wings.
- Most birds can fly.

Reptiles

These are the features of **reptiles**:

- They lay eggs on land. Their eggs have a leathery shell.
- They breathe air and live mainly on land.
- They have a scaly, dry skin.
- Reptiles like lizards move around to control their body temperature. Sometimes they sunbathe to warm up, but if it is very hot they shelter from the sun.

Amphibians

These are the features of **amphibians**:

- They lay jelly-like eggs in water.
- They breathe air and live partly on land but have to lay their eggs in water.
- They have a smooth, moist skin.

Fish

These are the features of **fish**:

- They can only live in water. They lay eggs in water.
- They breathe through gills.
- They have scales and fins.

Questions

1. In which vertebrate group are humans? Explain your answer.

2. What features do all birds have in common?

3. Describe a crocodile's skin.

4. Why do salamanders go back to water in the spring? Do you think all amphibians do this? Explain your answer.

5. How does a fish such as a salmon breathe?

6. Why do birds and reptiles have eggs with shells, but humans don't?

7. Give three features that make an amphibian different from a reptile.

For your notes

Vertebrates are classified into five groups.

The groups are **mammals**, **birds**, **reptiles**, **amphibians** and **fish**.

Each group has different features.

Make no bones about it

Invertebrates

The **invertebrate** animals have no backbones. They have no legs or lots of legs. The best way to start to classify them is to look for their legs!

No legs

We can start to sort the invertebrates with no legs into groups by the kind of body they have. Some have hard bodies, others have soft bodies. They also have different shaped bodies. There are six groups.

Invertebrate group		Body
Jellyfish		Soft jelly-like body
Starfish		Hard star-shaped body
Flatworms		Soft flat leaf-shaped body
Roundworms		Soft thin round body
Segmented worms		Soft body divided into rings called segments
Molluscs		Soft muscular body with one foot. Most have a hard shell.

Jointed legs

We call the invertebrates with lots of jointed legs **arthropods**. Arthropods have bodies made of sections called **segments**. We divide the arthropods into four smaller groups:

Arthropod group		Number of legs	Body
Crustaceans		Lots of legs	Soft body, usually with a hard shell
Centipedes and millipedes		Lots of legs	Segmented body
Spiders		8 legs	Body segments grouped to make a 2-part body
Insects		6 legs	Body segments grouped to make a 3-part body

Cuvier collection

Cuvier put all the sea shells together and called these Mollusca. He called all the insects, spiders and crabs Articulata (Latin for 'jointed'). All the other small creatures he called Radiata.

Did you know?

There are three times as many kinds of insect on the Earth as all the other animals put together.

Questions

1. a What feature do we use to classify invertebrates with no legs?

b An earthworm has no legs and a soft body with segments. In which group does it belong?

2. a What is an arthropod?

b What is the difference between a centipede and a roundworm?

3. Cuvier's microscopes were not as powerful as modern ones. Why do you think his classification was different from ours today?

4. *Challenge:* design a key to identify the arthropod groups. Use your key to find out which arthropod group this animal belongs to.

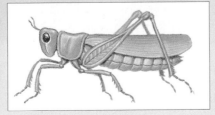

For your notes

Invertebrates are classified into seven groups.

The groups are **jellyfish, starfish, flatworms, roundworms, segmented worms, molluscs** and **arthropods**.

The arthropod group is divided into **crustaceans, centipedes** and **millipedes, spiders** and **insects**.

Species

We have seen how we group living things together by the similar features they have. However, there are lots of differences within groups of living things.

If there are enough differences between groups, we call them different **species**. Wolves and reindeer are different species. They cannot mate to produce a 'wolfdeer' or a 'reinolf'!

Wolf   *Reindeer*

The same but different

The humans in this crowd all belong to the same species because many of their features are similar.

a In what ways are the people in this crowd the same?

No two people are exactly alike – not even identical twins!

b In what ways are the people in this crowd different?

We are all different

We all belong to the species called *Homo sapiens*. We have different coloured eyes and hair. We have different weights and heights. Some of us are cleverer than others. Some of us are better at sport. Differences like these are called **variation**.

Each one of us is different because different features are passed on to us from our parents. These are **inherited features**. We are also different because we have grown up in different **surroundings**. Eating the wrong sort of food can make people fatter. This is an example of how things in our surroundings or lifestyle can cause variations.

c Give another three ways in which our surroundings or how we are brought up can affect the way we look.

Some features can only be one thing or the other, for example, hair may be straight or curly. We call this **discontinuous variation**. Other features vary gradually, with lots of in-betweens. This kind of variation is called **continuous variation**. Examples include height and weight.

Questions

1. What differences are there between wolves and reindeer?

2. Why do you think that you cannot mate a polar bear with a seal, but you can mate a polar bear with a brown bear?

3. Humans are all the same species, so why are there so many differences between us?

4. What features do you think are affected by our surroundings or how we are brought up?

5. Do these features show discontinuous variation or continuous variation?
   a eye colour   **b** straight or curly hair

For your notes

We call the differences between living things **variation**.

If there are enough differences between organisms, they are different **species**.

Some variations between the members of a species are **inherited** from their parents, and some are caused by their **surroundings**.

Discontinuous variation means having either one feature or another. In **continuous variation**, there are lots of in-betweens.

Born to survive

Paws for thought

A polar bear goes out without a care
of what clothes he should wear.
With only his thick white coat
– not even a scarf around his throat!
His colour is white to hide in the snow
from hunters he does not know.
Sitting on the edge of the ice,
a sight of dinner would be nice.
If a seal appears, he is ready to stalk –
no time to bother with a knife and fork!

Learn about

▶ Adaptation

Did you know?

Polar bears in zoos have been known to turn green because algae have grown inside the hollow hairs!

Adaptation

The place where an animal lives is called its **habitat**. The polar bear's habitat is the Arctic. The polar bear has a thick coat made of hollow hair. Each hollow hair is full of air, which acts as an insulator by trapping heat energy. This helps it survive in the cold North Pole snow and in the freezing Arctic sea with its packed ice. Having features that are suited to a habitat is called **adaptation**.

Camouflage

The polar bear's coat is white, so it does not show up against the snow. Other animals, including humans, cannot see the polar bear very easily. We call this **camouflage**. This is another adaptation. A baby seal has a white coat, so it cannot be seen in the snow. The adult seal grows a short, sleek, black coat that gives better camouflage against the dark sea. The mother instinctively knows when her baby is ready to swim. Read the poem from *The Jungle Book* which describes this.

From *The Jungle Book* by Rudyard Kipling

You mustn't swim till you're six weeks old,
Or your head will be sunk by your heels;
And summer gales and Killer Whales
Are bad for baby seals.

Are bad for baby seals, dear rat,
As bad as bad can be;
But splash and grow strong,
And you can't be wrong,
Child of the Open Sea!

a What could happen to a baby seal if it swam straight away?

b Write a paragraph to explain why camouflage is important to the baby seal using these three words:

predator   **prey**   **parenting**

Other adaptations

Many animals can **adapt** (change) to cope with different seasons and weather.

In the Arctic there are foxes, hares, caribou (we call them reindeer) and long-haired cattle called musk. They all have long hair or thick fur to keep them warm. The arctic fox and the arctic hare grow longer white fur for the winter. This hair falls out in the summer. This is called **moulting**.

In the Arctic sea there are seals and whales. They have a thick layer of fat called **blubber** to **insulate** them and keep them warm.

The other extreme

In contrast with the Arctic, the Sahara desert is very hot during the day. At night it is very cold. Animals that live in the desert must be able to adapt to daily changes in temperature and very dry conditions.

In the desert, some animals change their behaviour according to the temperature. Gerbils burrow into the desert sand to avoid the midday heat. Camels face the Sun at midday, exposing the minimum body surface to the Sun's rays.

c Look at the photo on the left. Why is the lizard sheltering under the rock?

Questions

1. Explain how the polar bear is adapted to keep warm in winter.

2. How does the colour of the polar bear's coat help it to survive?

3. Describe how some other animals are adapted to survive in the Arctic.

4. The baby seal's coat changes colour as it grows. Explain how this is an advantage to the seal.

5. Name three animals that change their behaviour to avoid the heat of the midday Sun. Explain how each one changes its behaviour.

6. Plan an experiment to find out whether fat is a good insulator. You have available the usual laboratory apparatus and a packet of cheese slices.

For your notes

Many animals are **adapted** to survive in their **habitat**.

Some animals are adapted to survive in the cold. They have fur or fat to **insulate** them from the cold.

Some animals are **camouflaged** to hide from other animals.

Some animals change their behaviour to help them cope with changes in temperature.

The right size?

Eskimo pen pal

Biork lives in Alaska, close to the Arctic Circle. Biork's ancestors are called Eskimos or Inuit people. Biork's people have survived the cold Arctic conditions for thousands of years. Biork's grandfather used to go out hunting for seals. He wore clothes made out of animal skins and built overnight shelters out of ice to keep warm.

Inuit people are born with short compact bodies. It's a feature that has been passed on through our families.

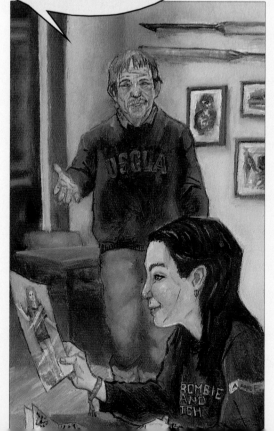

Why are Inuit people small?

The Inuit people have short, heavy, compact bodies. Biork has often wondered why she is small. She would like to be tall and thin like her pen friend in Florida. Biork's grandfather says it's a feature that helps them keep warm.

Biork's body shape is inherited from her parents, but it also depends on her surroundings, lifestyle and upbringing. Lots of variables can affect our height and weight. Some of these are:

- food – Inuits eat mainly seal's meat, which is very fatty

- exercise – if it is very cold, you stay inside. If you move around less, you do not use up so much food.

- seasons – children grow less in the winter because they use more of the chemical energy they get from their food to keep warm

- illness and stress can make you lose weight.

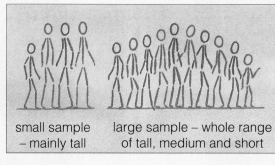

small sample – mainly tall   large sample – whole range of tall, medium and short

Research

A group of Canadian scientists studied the heights of more than 150 Inuit children. They compared them with a sample of children in the USA. It was important to take as large a sample as possible. If you take a small sample, you might get mainly tall people or mainly small people. If you take a large sample, you are more likely to see the whole **range** of different heights.

a Why do you think it is better to study a sample of 150 children from each place rather than only 10?

b How would you choose the children that you were going to study?

Making comparisons

When they had collected their data, the scientists compared the tallest 10% of each sample and the smallest 10% of each sample. They did this to see the differences.

Analysing the results

The graph shows the data for the Inuit girls compared with girls in the USA.

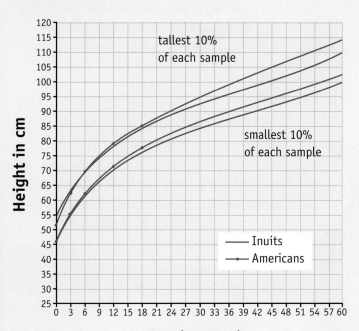

Age in months

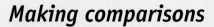
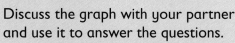
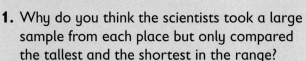

When both groups of children are 12 months old, the lines on the graph for the Inuit children and the American children are close together. This means that their heights are similar. After this, the lines are further apart, showing that the American children are taller.

Questions

Discuss the graph with your partner and use it to answer the questions.

1. Why do you think the scientists took a large sample from each place but only compared the tallest and the shortest in the range?

2. Was there any difference in the heights of the Inuit and the American girls when they were 12 months old?

3. What do you notice about the growth of the Inuit and the American girls between the ages of 12 and 60 months?

4. How do you think the data for boys might differ from the data for girls?

5. The scientists wanted to find out whether the Inuits are small because size is inherited. What other data might they have collected and analysed? Explain why you made your suggestions.

6. Do you think Biork's grandfather was right? Give two reasons for your answer.

7. Could you use your graph to predict the height of the Inuit girls when they are 30?

The burning question

Bonfire night

> I'm looking forward to the bonfire at the community centre. People have been piling up the branches and twigs for days. All of my family are going and so is my friend Deepak and his family.

> My family will be celebrating Divali, the festival of light. During the festival of light, my mum lights a candle on the window sill.

> Last year it rained on bonfire night. The bonfire was really wet and it took ages to light. I remember the fireworks with their dancing colours, green and lilac and bright white flashes. The fire was still burning when we all went home.

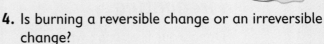

Questions

1. **a** List some materials as well as wood that people might burn on a bonfire.
   b Some materials don't burn very well. What things would not burn if you put them on a bonfire?

2. Why did the bonfire Dave went to last year take ages to light?

3. What kinds of energy are given out by:
   a a bonfire?
   b a candle?
   c fireworks?

4. Is burning a reversible change or an irreversible change?

5. What do you think happens when materials burn?

6. Do you think materials become lighter or heavier when they burn?

7. How could you show that a burning substance produces invisible gases?

8. If someone's clothes are on fire, why do you think rolling them in a blanket puts out the flames?

Oxygen

Is air needed for burning? Look at the picture. Three jars of different sizes are placed over a burning candle.

candle went out
after 10 seconds

candle went out
after 8 seconds

candle went out
after 4 seconds

(a) How does the amount of air available to the candle affect how long it burns?

The candle under the biggest jar burned for the longest time, because it had the most air. A candle needs air to burn.

Burning uses up part of the air. Air is a mixture of invisible gases. Burning materials use up one of the gases. It is the same gas that we need to stay alive.

The gas in air that is used up when materials burn is **oxygen**.

(b) Look at the pie chart. How much of air is oxygen?

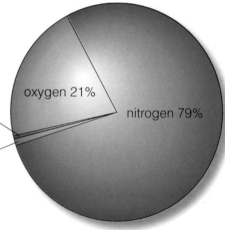

carbon
dioxide 0.4%

other gases
less than 1%

oxygen 21%

nitrogen 79%

Firefighting

Dangerous fires start when burning gets out of control. They produce large amounts of energy as heat and light. The fire in the building uses up the oxygen. The smoke and carbon dioxide made are also very dangerous. People trapped in a burning building cannot breathe. Firefighters sometimes have a cylinder of oxygen on their backs, so that they can breathe in a burning building.

Flammable materials

Some materials burn more easily than others. We call these **flammable** materials. Chemicals that are flammable have a hazard warning label on the container. This gives a clear warning to people, whatever language they speak.

Some synthetic materials such as plastics and polyester fabrics give off poisonous gases when they burn. Polyester and nylon melt and stick to the skin. It is important to keep all furniture and clothes away from gas fires and heaters.

The fire triangle

A burning material acts as a **fuel**. A fuel gives out large amounts of energy as heat and light when it burns.

You need three things to make a fire burn:

- fuel
- oxygen
- heat.

The fire triangle shows the things you need to make a fire.

To put a fire out, you have to break the triangle by taking away one side – the fuel, the oxygen or the heat.

Questions

1. What is the name of the gas in the air needed for life and for burning?

2. Why do firefighters carry oxygen cylinders?

3. Explain the meaning of the word 'flammable'. Draw and label the flammable hazard warning symbol.

4. The fabrics used for furniture, curtains and children's pyjamas are treated with flame-proofing chemicals. Why do you think this is done?

5. What three things does a fire need to burn? Draw the fire triangle.

6. Firefighters often put fires out with water. Which part of the fire triangle are they taking away?

For your notes

The part of the air needed for burning is called **oxygen**. Oxygen is also needed for life.

Flammable materials burn more easily than others.

Fires need fuel, oxygen and heat to burn.

Burning changes

Chemical change

Have you ever looked at the remains of a bonfire next day?

After a bonfire has finished burning, all that remains is ash and soot. There may be pieces of metal or brick which have turned black. You cannot get the wood back from the ash – burning is an irreversible change. Burning is a **chemical change**. When a chemical change happens, you cannot get back the substance you started with.

The substances left behind in the ash are called **oxides**. When a substance burns, it joins with oxygen in the air to make an oxide. The name 'oxide' comes from the word 'oxygen'. We take the first two letters of oxygen and add 'ide'.

Fireworks

Metals burn to make oxides. We use metals in fireworks because they give out flashes, sparks and colours.

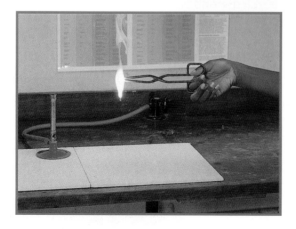

Magnesium

Magnesium is a silvery coloured metal. It burns to give a white flash which is very bright. You have to look at it through blue glass or it will damage your eyes.

Flash bulbs for cameras have magnesium inside them. Magnesium burns in air to give a new substance called **magnesium oxide**. This new substance is made by a **chemical reaction**. You cannot change it back easily.

Writing a word equation

When magnesium burns, the magnesium and oxygen are changed into magnesium oxide. We can write a **word equation** for this reaction.

> magnesium + oxygen → magnesium oxide

The substances that react are on the left. The substances that are made are on the right. The substances on the left react together to make the substances on the right.

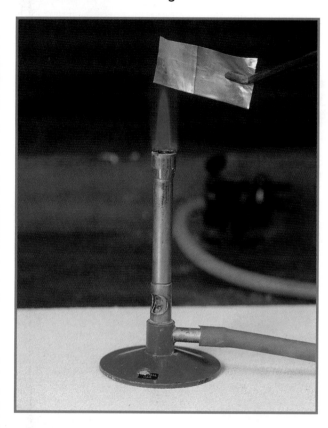

Iron

When iron burns, it gives out sparks. Fireworks like the sparkler in the photo have iron powder in them. The name of the new substance formed is **iron oxide**.

Copper

The photo opposite shows copper being heated. Copper becomes coated with a black substance when you hold it in a flame. Have you ever noticed how copper bracelets gradually turn black when you wear them? When you burn substances that have copper in them, the flame looks greenish.

The copper combines with the oxygen in the air to form **copper oxide**.

Questions

1. What does a bonfire look like after it has finished burning?

2. What sort of substances does ash contain? How are they formed?

3. How do we know that burning is a chemical change?

4. Why do we use metals to make fireworks?

5. Write down what happens when you burn:
   a magnesium   b iron   c copper.

6. Write a word equation for the reaction that takes place when these metals burn:
   a iron   b copper.

For your notes

Substances join with oxygen to make **oxides**. This is a **chemical change**.

Some metals burn in air to make oxides.

Fuels store energy

A **fuel** is a substance that stores a lot of chemical energy. When the fuel burns, it releases **heat energy** or **light energy** which we can use. The human body uses food as a fuel.

Jenny's holiday diary

Friday
Dad spent all day packing the car before we set off. Mum made him go to the garage and fill up with petrol because she didn't want to run out before we got to the ferry port.

Saturday (morning)
We were excited and got up early. Mum told us to eat a good breakfast as we would need the energy for the journey. I had cereal and milk as usual. William had bacon, sausage and baked beans. Mum and Dad settled for boiled eggs and toast.

Saturday (lunchtime)
There was an enormous queue on the ferry boat for cooked lunch, so we only had a sandwich from the snack bar.

Saturday (evening)
It was 9 o'clock in the evening when we finally reached the camp site because we got lost and couldn't get any gas for the camping stove. William was so hungry that he ate his last bar of chocolate. I just fell asleep ...

a Make a list of all the fuels Jenny mentioned.
(Hint: include foods.)

How much energy is in food?

When we eat food, the body uses it as fuel. Food gives us energy to keep warm and move around. Jenny's family used the energy from their breakfast to think, rest, move and play on the first part of the trip.

We measure energy in units called **joules**, **J**. There are 1000 J in 1 **kilojoule**, **kJ**. Different foods contain different amounts of energy. Sausages contain much more energy than breakfast cereal. You can measure how much energy there is in food.

How much energy is in fuels?

We burn different fuels to keep warm, light our houses and roads or make things move. Different fuels give out different amounts of energy. A small piece of coal gives out more energy than a small piece of wood. The pictures show some different fuels being used.

candle

barbecue

camping gas   petrol

Did you know?

Each person in the UK uses about 17 million kilojoules of energy each day, in fuels and food.

Barbecue time

The fuel for a barbecue is charcoal. Charcoal is a fuel because it has a store of energy. This **chemical energy** stays in the charcoal until you light it. When you light the charcoal, the energy comes out as heat energy and light energy. The heat energy is transferred from the charcoal to the food, making it hot.

Questions

1. Make a list of fuels we use, and what they are used for.

2. What makes charcoal a fuel?

3. When you burn charcoal, what kind of energy do you want to use? What kind of energy is wasted energy?

4. Which gives out more joules of energy per gram when you burn it, coal or wood?

5. Write down some of the ways Jenny's family might have used the energy in their food.

For your notes

Fuels store energy. Energy is released when fuels burn. There are many different fuels.

The body uses food as fuel.

We measure energy in **joules, J**.

55

What's special about fuels?

Before and after

In the days before central heating, most people lit a fire every morning. First they screwed up some paper, and then placed wooden sticks on top. Finally they put on a few lumps of coal and lit the paper with a match.

The paper started the wood burning, and then the coal started to burn. The coal burned steadily, giving out the most heat energy.

No one really liked clearing up next day. Cleaning out the grey ash was a messy job.

Coal

Some people still have coal fires in their homes. Coal is a black, shiny, rocky substance. It comes from dead trees. The trees were squashed under the ground and gradually changed to coal. This took millions of years. Coal has to be dug out of the ground by coal miners.

Some coal produces fumes and lots of smoke when it burns. Smoke is unburned coal. Coal may be heated to make 'smokeless' fuel which produces less smoke. Smokeless fuels are quite expensive.

The Clean Air Act of 1956 is a law that says some residential areas have to be smokeless zones. It is illegal to burn 'ordinary' coal in these areas.

a Suggest reasons why central heating is more common now than coal fires.

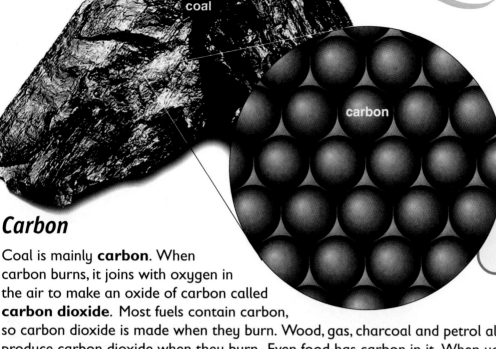

coal

carbon

Did you know?

We mine 3000 million tonnes of coal each year. At this rate coal will last for about 300 years before it is all used up.

Carbon

Coal is mainly **carbon**. When carbon burns, it joins with oxygen in the air to make an oxide of carbon called **carbon dioxide**. Most fuels contain carbon, so carbon dioxide is made when they burn. Wood, gas, charcoal and petrol all produce carbon dioxide when they burn. Even food has carbon in it. When your body uses food as fuel, energy is released and carbon dioxide is made.

Carbon dioxide

Carbon dioxide is an invisible gas. Unlike oxygen, it is not needed for burning. It puts fires out!

Carbon dioxide is more dense ('heavier') than air. It sinks and covers the fuel, stopping the oxygen getting to it. A carbon dioxide fire extinguisher should be pointed directly over the flames to cover the fuel with carbon dioxide gas.

You can test for carbon dioxide with a solution called **limewater**. First you have to collect the gas. You trap it in a funnel and pass it along a tube into the limewater. As the carbon dioxide gas bubbles through the limewater, the solution turns milky white.

Questions

1. Why is coal a good fuel?

2. Where does coal come from? How was it formed?

3. What do most fuels contain? How do we know this?

4. How could you show that a burning fuel gives out carbon dioxide?

5. Explain how a carbon dioxide fire extinguisher puts a fire out. Include a tip for effective use.

For your notes

The fuels we burn contain **carbon**, and so does food.

When carbon burns, it joins with oxygen in the air to make **carbon dioxide**.

Carbon dioxide is a gas which turns **limewater** milky.

It's all about reactions

Particles

Coal is mainly carbon. Carbon is made of carbon particles. Oxygen is made of oxygen particles. Coal burns when you light it because energy is transferred to the particles. They move faster and bump into each other. Each carbon particle joins with two oxygen particles to make carbon dioxide. 'Di' means two, so 'dioxide' means two particles of oxygen. Carbon dioxide is a new substance.

oxygen particle

carbon particle

carbon dioxide

Chemical reactions

When different particles join together to make new substances, we call it a **chemical reaction**. Burning is a chemical reaction. The chemical name for burning is **combustion**.

On the left are one carbon particle and two oxygen particles.

They add together and react.

On the right is carbon dioxide made from one carbon particle and two oxygen particles joined together.

| carbon | + | oxygen | → | carbon dioxide |

The **word equation** above shows what is happening in the combustion reaction. The amount on the left of the equation is the same as the amount on the right of the equation. We say the equation **balances**.

In maths, we write equations to show numbers adding together. Both sides of the equation balance. In a chemical reaction, there are the same number of particles on both sides of the equation. The mass is the same on both sides.

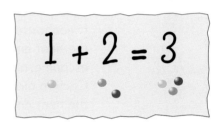

Burning other fuels

We have already seen that some fuels, such as coal, are mostly carbon. When they burn they produce carbon dioxide.

Fuels such as wax, petrol and oil are called **hydrocarbons**. The 'hydro' part means they contain hydrogen as well as carbon. Food also contains hydrogen. When hydrocarbons burn, the carbon joins with oxygen to produce carbon dioxide. The hydrogen also joins with oxygen to produce 'hydrogen oxide', which we know as water. Water contains hydrogen and oxygen particles.

We can write a word equation for this part of the reaction:

> hydrogen + oxygen → water

If we put both parts of the reaction together, we can write a general word equation for the combustion of hydrocarbon fuels:

> fuel + oxygen → carbon dioxide + water

Petrol and oil are both hydrocarbons.

Questions

1. Explain how we know that burning is a chemical reaction.

2. What is the scientific name for burning?

3. Why do we have to light coal before it burns?

4. What happens when a fuel burns?

5. Hydrogen is used as rocket fuel. Write a word equation for the reaction when rocket fuel burns.

For your notes

When a fuel burns, a **chemical reaction** called **combustion** takes place.

A **word equation** shows what happens in a chemical reaction.

Equations must **balance**.

Hydrocarbons are fuels that contain carbon and hydrogen.

Burning

4.7

Getting hotter

Fuels in industry

We burn large amounts of fuels such as coal, oil and gas to give us light energy, heat energy and to make things move. The more fuels we burn, the more carbon dioxide we release into the air.

The greenhouse effect

The carbon dioxide in the air has the same effect as the glass in a greenhouse. The glass stops some of the heat energy in the greenhouse escaping, and the plants stay warm. Carbon dioxide stops some of the heat energy from the Earth escaping, and the Earth stays warm. This is called the **greenhouse effect**.

Scientists think that too much carbon dioxide will increase the greenhouse effect and the Earth will get too hot. They think that there is a relationship between the level of carbon dioxide in the air and the temperature of the Earth. As the level of carbon dioxide rises, the Earth gets hotter.

The biodome experiment

A team of students decided to find out whether there is a relationship between the temperature of the Earth and carbon dioxide levels in the atmosphere. It is difficult to measure large-scale changes around the Earth, so they designed a **model** to represent the Earth.

Think about

➤ Relationships between variables

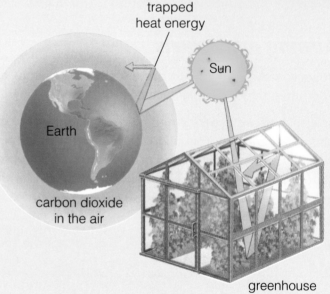

greenhouse

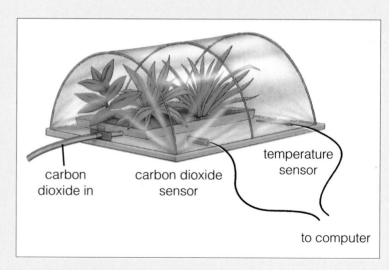

carbon dioxide in

carbon dioxide sensor

temperature sensor

to computer

They set up a biodome, as shown in the diagram. Carbon dioxide can be added through the tube at the side. The carbon dioxide level and the temperature inside the dome are recorded by a computer.

60

Any relationship?

(a) Can you identify the input and outcome variables in the biodome experiment?

We use the word **relationship** to describe how the outcome variable changes when we change the input variable.

The students ran the experiment for 5 days. They increased the level of carbon dioxide each day to see if there was a relationship between carbon dioxide level and temperature. The graph on the computer screen looked like this.

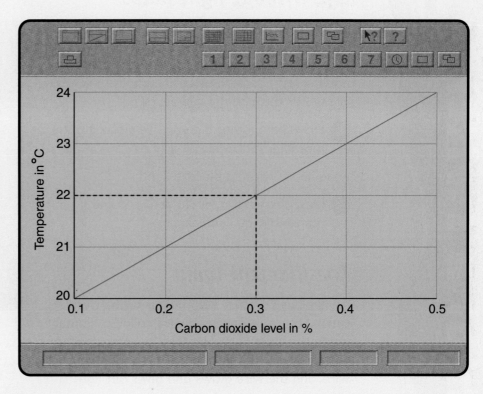

Describing the graph

A **relationship** describes how the outcome variable changes when the input variable is changed. It describes the pattern shown by a graph.

The graph of temperature against carbon dioxide level shows a relationship. On the first day, the carbon dioxide level went up by 0.1% and the temperature went up by 1 °C. This happened every day. The carbon dioxide level and the temperature both went up together. This gives a straight-line graph.

(b) Look at the graph. What was the temperature in the biodome when the carbon dioxide level was 0.3%? Follow the line up from 0.3% on the x-axis and stop when it touches the graph. Then follow the line across to the y-axis to find out the temperature.

If the students had carried out the experiment for a few more days, the line of the graph would have continued to show the same pattern.

Questions

Discuss the questions with a partner. Jot down your answers.

1. What do you think the temperature in the biodome would have been when the carbon dioxide level was 1.0%? (You are making a prediction.)

2. Do you think there is a relationship between carbon dioxide levels and the temperature of the Earth? Why do you think that?

3. Use the results from the biodome to predict what you think will happen to the temperature of the Earth over the next 10 years.

4. What do you think the scientists should do next?

5. Find out how the greenhouse effect could affect:

   a polar ice-caps

   b weather

   c world food supplies.

At the touch of a switch

Life without light bulbs

Imagine life without electricity. There would be no television, computers, washing machines or microwaves. Even gas central heating would not work: it needs an electric pump to move the hot water through the radiators.

a How many times did you use electricity this morning? Make a list.

Imagine life without electric light.

b Describe what it would be like doing your homework by candlelight.

The filament lamp

An ordinary electric light bulb is a **filament lamp**. There is a piece of wire called a filament inside the glass bulb. This wire becomes part of a circuit when you put the bulb in a socket. The electricity heats the wire, and the wire glows and gives out light.

c What happens to a filament lamp when the filament breaks? Why?

Using different filaments

Humphry Davy.

Humphry Davy made light using electricity in 1801. He put strips of platinum in a circuit. The electricity made the strips of metal heat up and glow. Unfortunately, the metal burned, so the light went out.

Joseph Swan.

In 1850 Joseph Swan tried filaments of paper covered with carbon, but the filament burned away in the air. The lamp would only work if the filament was kept away from air.

Working separately, Joseph Swan and Thomas Edison both thought of enclosing the filament in a glass bulb and pumping all the air out. This was only possible after 1875, when the pump they needed was invented.

The first successful electric light bulbs were made by Swan in 1878 and Edison in 1879. They both used a wire of carbon as the filament. The filament was sealed in a glass bulb with no air inside, so the carbon glowed rather than burned.

In 1911 the carbon filament was replaced by a tungsten filament, which lasted longer. Then in 1913 the filaments were coiled, so there was more wire to glow.

d What was wrong with Humphry Davy's idea of using strips of platinum as a filament?

e Joseph Swan's carbon and paper filaments did not last more than a few minutes. Why?

f Why was all the air pumped out of the light bulb?

g Why were carbon filaments replaced with tungsten filaments?

h Why is a coiled filament better than a straight filament?

Questions

1. How is an electric filament lamp better than a candle?

2. Electric filament bulbs:
- give out bright light
- give out a lot of thermal energy
- are cheap
- break when dropped
- 'blow' after they have been used for a long time.

How could the electric filament bulb be improved?

3. Use the information on these pages to make a time line entitled 'The invention and development of the electric filament lamp'.

4. Streetlights used to be gas lamps, a bit like a Bunsen burner with the hole closed. A person called a lamplighter used to light the lamps each evening and turn them out each morning. Imagine you are a lamplighter and the streetlights are being replaced with electric filament lamps. These lamps will be switched on and off from a central control point. Write a letter to a friend explaining how you feel about these modern streetlights.

Energy from electricity

Electricity carries energy to make things work.

In the picture, the battery is making the lamp light.

a Write an energy transfer diagram for lighting a lamp using a battery. Remember that batteries store chemical energy.

Look back to page 7 if you need a reminder.

Look back to page 7 if you need a reminder.

Learn about

► Circuits

The energy must be transferred along the wires to the lamp.

The energy comes from the battery.

Electricity carries energy to make things work.

The lamp transfers light energy and thermal energy.

Making connections

You can join batteries and a lamp in many different ways.

b Look at the drawings below. Give the letters of the lamps that will light up.

c Three lamps do not light because the circuit is not complete. Give the letters of these lamps.

d One lamp does not light because the batteries are connected wrongly. Which lamp is this?

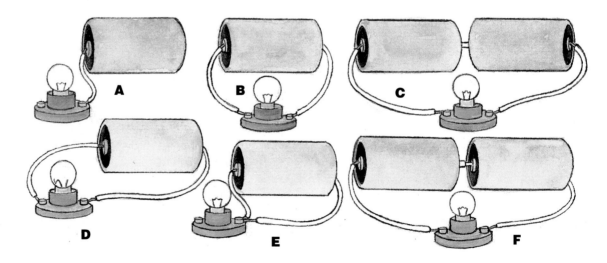

A B C D E F

To make the lamp light, there must be a **complete circuit**. The battery, the wires and the lamp must make a closed loop. This loop includes the filament of the lamp. If the filament is broken, as in lamp **D**, the circuit is broken and the lamp will not light.

You need a complete circuit to transfer energy from the battery to the lamp.

Circuit symbols

Drawing lamps, batteries and switches takes a long time. It is easier to draw circuits with these simple symbols.

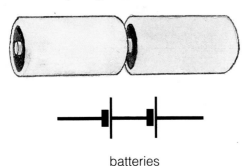

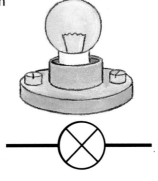

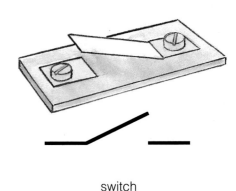

batteries   lamp   switch

Questions

1. Draw circuit **X** shown opposite using symbols.

circuit **X**

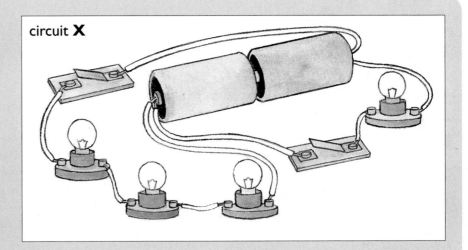

2. Look at circuit **Y**. All the lamps light when all the switches are closed. All the switches are shown open.

  a How many lamps are there in this circuit?

  b How many switches are there in this circuit?

  c Copy and complete this table.

circuit **Y**

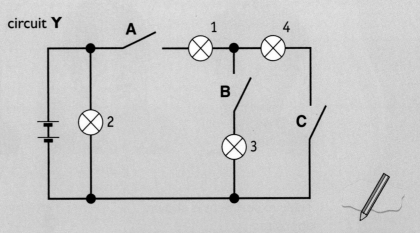

Switches closed	Lamps lit
A, B, C	1, 2, 3
None	
A, C	
A, B	
A	

3. Jane has a torch that does not work. Write down all the faults that could stop the torch working. How could Jane check for each of the faults?

For your notes

We get energy from electricity to make things work.

You need a **complete circuit** for energy to be transferred.

Current

You need a complete circuit to transfer energy from the battery to the lamp. We are going to learn about what is happening in the circuit. Electricity flows in the wires. We call this a **current**.

We can show the current in the wires by putting an **ammeter** in the circuit. An ammeter measures current in **amps**. The short way of writing amps is A. The circuit symbol for an ammeter is (A).

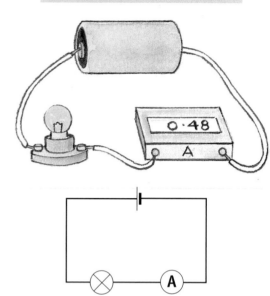

a Where do you put the ammeter to measure the current?

b What is current measured in?

Moving the ammeter

Ben, Laura and Dan were doing an experiment about current. Their teacher asked them where to put the ammeter in a circuit.

Does it matter where you put the ammeter?

It will have to be in the circuit. Let's put it to the left of the lamp.

It doesn't matter where you put it. The current is the same on both sides of the lamp.

No, energy leaves at the lamp. I think the current will be different on either side. Let's use two ammeters to check.

Ben   Laura   Dan

Their experiment is shown opposite.

c Is the current different or the same on each side of the lamp?

d Who was correct, Laura or Dan?

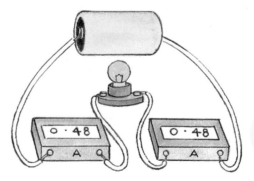

The current is the same on both sides of the lamp.

More complicated circuits

Laura and Dan decided to investigate this question:

● If you have more lamps, does the current change?

e Who predicts that the more lamps there are, the less current there will be?

f Who predicts that there is no relationship between the number of lamps and the current?

The circuits they used and their results are shown below.

It won't make a difference. There are lots of lamps at home and they are all bright. The current will stay the same.

Yes it will, the current gets reduced because it is going through more lamps. The more lamps, the less current.

Laura   Dan

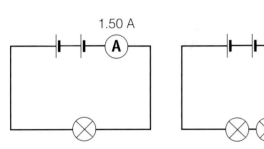
1.50 A   0.75 A

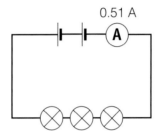
0.51 A

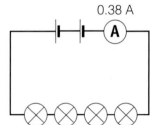
0.38 A

g Whose prediction was correct?

Ben and Lucy decided to investigate this question:

● If you have more batteries, does the current change?

The circuits they used and their results are shown below.

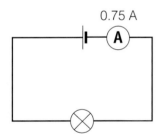
0.75 A

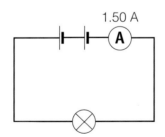
1.50 A

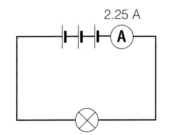
2.25 A

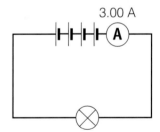
3.00 A

h What happens when you put more batteries in the circuit?

Questions

1. Use Laura and Dan's results to plot a line graph of current against number of lamps. Put the number of lamps along the bottom and the current up the side. Draw a curved line of best fit.

2. Use Ben and Lucy's results to plot a graph of current against number of batteries. Put the number of batteries along the bottom and the current up the side. Draw the line of best fit. It should be a straight line.

For your notes

Current is measured in **amps**, **A**, using an **ammeter**.

The current is the same on both sides of a lamp.

Increasing the number of lamps decreases the current.

Increasing the number of batteries increases the current.

Voltage

We have learned about current. Current is measured *in* the circuit using an ammeter. The ammeter is put *in* the circuit.

We can also measure **voltage**. Voltage is not measured *in* the circuit. It is measured *across* parts of the circuit. Voltage is measured with a **voltmeter**. The voltmeter is put *across* parts of the circuit.

Voltage is measured in **volts**. The short way of writing volts is **V**. The circuit symbol for a voltmeter is (V).

Energy in and out

Ben and Lucy measured the voltage across four parts of a circuit. The circuit is shown opposite. The circuit is shown in black, as usual. The wires going to the voltmeters are in pink. One voltmeter is across the lamp. One voltmeter is across the battery. The other two voltmeters are across wires. The circuit diagram shows this too.

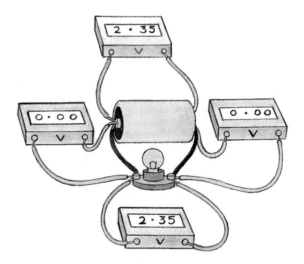

a What is the voltage across:
  i the lamp?
  ii the battery?
  iii the wires?

There is a voltage across the lamp because energy exits the circuit at the lamp. It leaves as light energy and thermal energy.

There is a voltage across the battery because energy enters the circuit at the battery. Batteries put electrical energy into the circuit.

There is no voltage across the wires. This is because no energy enters or exits the circuit at the wires.

Voltage tells us the change in the energy in the circuit.

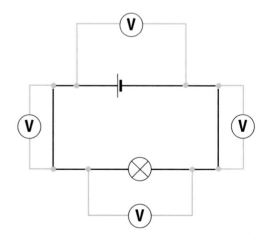

b Where is energy entering the circuit?

c Where is energy exiting the circuit?

d Why is there no voltage across the wires?

There is a voltage across any part of a circuit where energy is entering the circuit or where energy is exiting the circuit.

Batteries and voltage

Batteries put energy into circuits. If you connect a voltmeter across a battery, it will show a voltage.

Ellen and Jermaine investigated how increasing the number of batteries changed the voltage. They made three circuits: **A**, **B** and **C**. The batteries were all the same. The lamps were all the same.

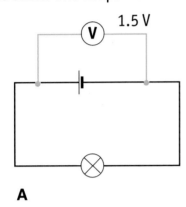

A

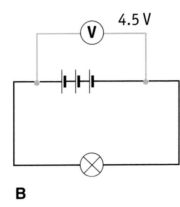

B

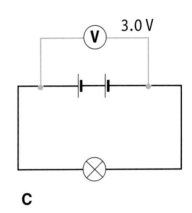

C

e Which voltmeter shows the biggest reading? Why?

f Which lamp would be brightest?

g Ellen made another circuit, this time with four batteries. Predict the reading on the voltmeter.

h Imagine another voltmeter, across the lamp in circuit **C**. What would be the reading on the voltmeter? How did you know this?

Questions

1. There were three lamps in a circuit. The lamps were not the same. Seth measured the voltage across each lamp.

Lamp	Voltage in V
A	1.5
B	2.5
C	2.0

Which lamp was giving out the most energy?

2. Zahid and Jo were given four boxes. Each box contained a different, unknown number of batteries. None of the boxes could hold more than eight batteries. Zahid and Jo measured the voltage across each box.

Box	A	B	C	D
Voltage in V	4.5	6.0	9.0	3.0

How many batteries were there in each box?

For your notes

Voltage is measured across parts of a circuit.

Voltage is measured in **volts, V**, using a **voltmeter**.

There is a voltage across any part of the circuit where energy is entering or exiting.

Using models

Scientists use **models** to help them think.
Each part of a model represents something in real life.

A good model fits with the facts. So far, you know these facts about electricity.

> Electricity carries energy to make things work.

> You need a complete circuit to transfer energy from a battery to make a lamp light.

> The current is the same on both sides of the lamp.

> There is a voltage across any part of a circuit where energy is entering the circuit or where energy is exiting the circuit.

Think about

➤ Models of electricity

The coal truck model

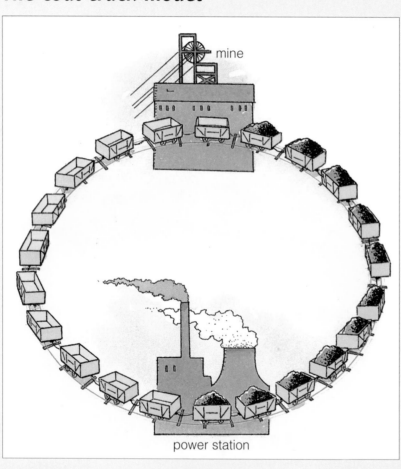

mine

power station

This model shows a mine and a power station. There is a single-track railway between the mine and the power station. Coal trucks run along the railway. The coal trucks can move quickly or slowly along the track.

At the mine, the coal trucks are filled with coal. The coal trucks run along the tracks and deliver the coal to the power station. The empty coal trucks then return to the mine.

Read the description carefully again and study the diagram. Then answer the questions.

a In the coal truck model, what represents:
  i the circuit?
  ii the battery?
  iii the lamp?
  iv the energy?

b The moving trucks represent the current. When the trucks speed up, does the current increase or decrease?

c Do you think there is anything in the model about voltage?

d Do you think this is a good model? Explain your answer.

The class and matches model

Mrs Fuller is using another model to explain electricity to her class.

Mrs Fuller gives each pupil a match as they pass her.

The pupils continue and collect another match.

The pupils carry their matches round the white circle.

Mrs Huxley strikes each match as the pupil passes it to her.

e Draw a diagram of this model. Use the same colours as in the coal truck model:
- energy is green
- the circuit is pink
- the current is yellow
- the voltage (where energy enters and exits) is blue.

f Does this model help you understand electricity? Explain your answer.

g Can you put an ammeter into your class and matches model? What would the ammeter do? Where would the ammeter be in your drawing?

h Can you put a voltmeter into your class and matches model? Explain.

Questions

1. Which was the better model for you, the coal truck model or the class and matches model? Explain your answer.

2. Can you think of another model for electricity? Draw a diagram to explain your model. (Other people have suggested a roller coaster or a bicycle.)

More circuits

Series and parallel circuits

There are two ways of connecting two lamps and a battery.

You can put the lamps side by side, as shown here.

This is called a **series** circuit.

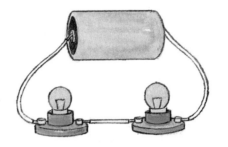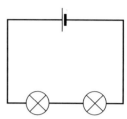

You can put the lamps in different loops, as here.

This is called a **parallel** circuit.

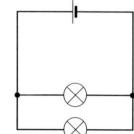

Suzy and John compared series and parallel circuits. They used identical batteries and identical lamps. They found that the lamps were brighter in the parallel circuit.

Current in series and parallel circuits

series circuit

Y

A
0.1 A

A
0.1 A

X
A
0.1 A

parallel circuit

P

0.4 A
A

0.4 A
A

Q
0.2 A
A

R
0.2 A
A

Kimberly and Jason investigated current in series and parallel circuits. They used identical batteries and two identical lamps in each circuit.

In the series circuit, they discovered that the current was the same at all points in the circuit. In the parallel circuit, the current was shared between the loops of the circuit.

a Look at the series circuit. What would the current be at **X** and at **Y**?

b Look at the parallel circuit. What would the current be at **P**, at **Q** and at **R**?

Voltage in series and parallel circuits

Moomith and Alan investigated voltage in series and parallel circuits. They used identical batteries and two identical lamps in each circuit.

In the series circuit, they discovered that the voltage across the battery is shared between the lamps. In the parallel circuit, they discovered that the voltage was the same across each lamp and across the battery.

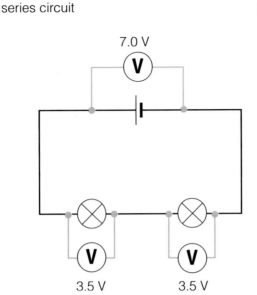

series circuit

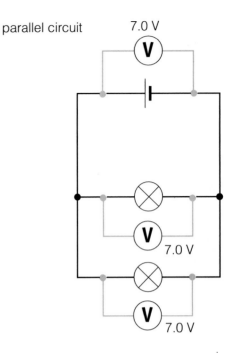

parallel circuit

c Imagine two more identical lamps were put into the series circuit. Predict the voltage across each lamp.

d Imagine a third loop with another identical lamp added to the parallel circuit. Predict the voltage across this third lamp.

Questions

1. Make a table with the headings 'Series circuits' and 'Parallel circuits'. Fill in the table to compare:

   - lamp brightness
   - number of loops
   - voltage
   - current.

2. You have two lamps and three switches. You want to make a parallel circuit that will:

   - switch off both lamps together

   and also:

   - switch off each lamp separately.

   Draw the circuit that will do this.

3. **a** Look back at the models for electricity on pages 70–71. Try to use one of the models to explain series and parallel circuits. Include a diagram and labels to explain what is happening.

   b Does the model work for series and parallel circuits?

For your notes

You can connect lamps in **series** and in **parallel**. Parallel circuits have more than one loop.

Lamps in parallel are brighter than the same lamps in series, using the same battery.

In a series circuit:

- the current is the same at all points
- the voltage is shared between the lamps.

In a parallel circuit:

- the current is shared between the loops
- the voltage is the same across the battery and each lamp.

Magnets

Magnetic fields

You have probably discovered how a bar magnet acts when you put it near iron. A coil of wire with electricity passing through it acts like a magnet.

If you sprinkle iron filings around a magnet, you can see a pattern around the magnet. Iron filings are tiny pieces of iron. The pattern is made because the magnet attracts the tiny pieces of iron towards it. We say the magnet has a **magnetic field**. Only iron filings inside the magnetic field are attracted. Photo **A** shows the magnetic field around a bar magnet. Photo **B** shows the magnetic field around a coil of wire with electricity passing through it.

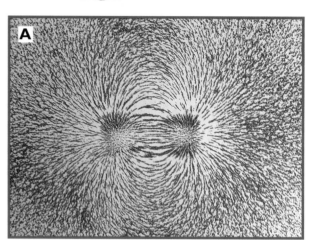

Both the bar magnet and the coil pull the iron filings into lines. We can show the lines by drawing **magnetic field lines**.

Magnetic field lines run from the **north pole** of the magnet to the **south pole** of the magnet. You can show the direction of the magnetic field lines using a compass. The photos below show this for a bar magnet (**C**) and a coil (**D**).

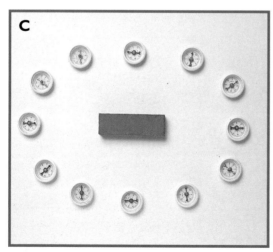

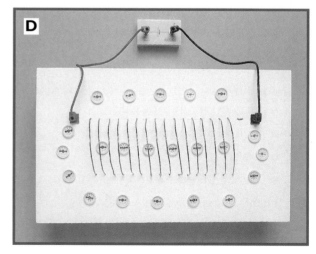

(a) Iron filings were sprinkled around two different magnets, **X** and **Y**. The magnetic field lines were much closer together for magnet **X** than magnet **Y**. Which was the stronger magnet?

(b) Look at photo **D**. What would happen if the current in the coil was turned off?

Magnets attract and repel

Two magnetic north poles push apart or **repel**. Two south poles repel. A north pole and a south pole pull together or **attract**. This is true of ordinary magnets (photo **E**) and the coil with the current (photo **F**).

c Imagine two magnets pushing apart. Draw the different ways the magnets could be arranged.

d Look at photo **F**. The two coils are pulling together. Why is this happening?

e What would happen if the current to the coils was switched off?

E

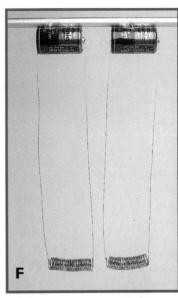

F

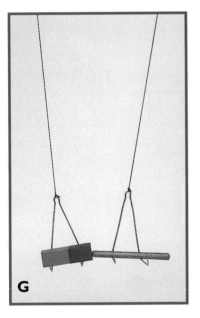

G

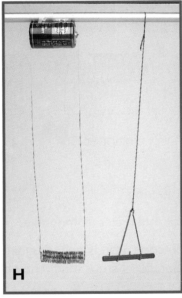

H

Magnetic materials

Magnets attract **magnetic materials**. Iron, nickel and cobalt are magnetic. Many metals contain some iron, nickel or cobalt so many metals are magnetic.

f Name three metals that will be attracted to a magnet.

The magnet and the coil attract a piece of iron.

Questions

1. What do we call:
   a the space around a magnet where iron filings are pulled?
   b the lines iron filings make near a magnet?
   c materials that are attracted to a magnet?
   d pushing apart?
   e pulling together?

2. A coil of wire with a current in it behaves like a magnet. Make a list of all the ways the coil behaves like an ordinary magnet. Then make a list of the ways it is different from an ordinary magnet.

For your notes

A coil of wire connected to a battery makes a magnet.

Magnets make **magnetic fields**. Magnetic fields have **magnetic field lines**.

Like magnetic poles **repel**. Unlike poles **attract**.

Iron, nickel and cobalt are **magnetic** metals.

Electromagnets

Electricity and magnetism

You can connect a coil to a battery so that the electric current runs through it. The coil behaves like a weak magnet. Putting a **core** of magnetic material inside the coil makes a stronger magnet. This is called an **electromagnet**. In the photo you can see how the electromagnet attracts the keys.

Core material

You can use any magnetic material for the core.

Craig carried out an investigation with electromagnets. He used different materials for the core. He coiled wire around each core material, connected the wire to a battery and tried to pick up paperclips. His results are shown below.

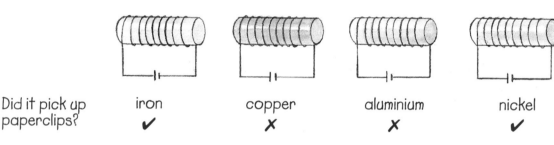

| Did it pick up paperclips? | iron ✔ | copper ✘ | aluminium ✘ | nickel ✔ |

a Which metals made electromagnets?

b Why did the other metals not make electromagnets?

Most electromagnets have an iron core. Iron is only magnetic when it is in a magnetic field. Steel is different. Steel stays magnetic after it is removed from the magnetic field.

c Why is steel unsuitable as the core of a magnet you want to turn off?

Stronger electromagnets: more batteries

Ruksham and Hannah wanted to make their electromagnet stronger. They increased the current by adding more batteries. They kept the same iron core and the same number of turns in the coil. The table shows Ruksham and Hannah's results.

Number of batteries	1	2	3	4	5
Current in A	0.2	0.4	0.6	0.8	1.0
Paperclips lifted	5	11	16	24	29

d Plot a line graph of Ruksham and Hannah's results. Put current along the bottom and paperclips lifted up the side. Draw a line of best fit. What do the results show?

e Ruksham and Hannah connect an electromagnet to a battery that makes a current of 0.7 A. Predict the number of paperclips they will pick up.

Stronger electromagnets: more turns

Gina and Scott also wanted to make their electromagnet stronger. They increased the number of turns in the coil. The table below shows their results.

Number of turns	10	20	30	40	50
Current in A	0.5	0.5	0.5	0.5	0.5
Paperclips lifted	3	9	16	31	40

f Plot a line graph of Gina and Scott's results. Put number of turns along the bottom and paperclips lifted up the side. Draw a line of best fit. What do the results show?

g Gina and Scott could make an electromagnet with 25 turns. Predict how many paperclips it will lift.

> **To make a strong electromagnet you need to:**
> - **have an iron core**
> - **increase the current**
> - **have lots of turns in the coil.**

Using electromagnets

Huge electromagnets like the one in the photo are used in scrap yards to pick up cars.

h Most cars are made of iron. Some modern cars are made of aluminium. What problem will this cause for scrap yard owners?

Questions

1. Electromagnets are used in scrap yards. Why would the electromagnet be made with an iron core rather than a steel core?

2. Write a conclusion for Craig's investigation shown on the opposite page. You should include:
   - a summary of his results
   - an explanation of why some cores worked and others did not
   - a suggestion for another experiment to check if your explanation is correct.

For your notes

An **electromagnet** is a coil of wire with an electric current running through it and a **core** inside.

Electromagnets are made with an iron core so that they can be switched off.

Increasing the current in the coil makes an electromagnet stronger.

Increasing the number of turns in the coil of an electromagnet also makes it stronger.

77

The history of microscopes

Small is beautiful

Before scientists had microscopes, they could not see things that are very small. They could only guess what things looked like.

In 1670 a Dutchman called Antoni van Leeuwenhoek made a simple microscope with one lens. He used this microscope to study small objects. His microscope was very popular. Scientists everywhere began to use microscopes like it. The word 'microscope' comes from *micro* which means small and *scope* which means look at.

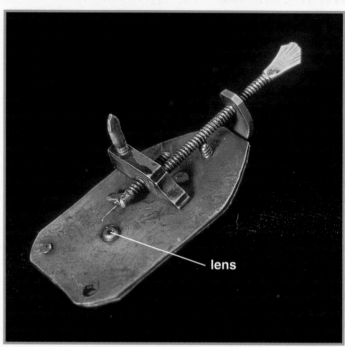

lens

Antoni van Leeuwenhoek's microscope.

The compound microscope

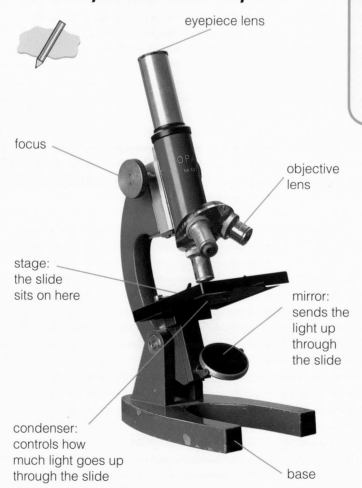

eyepiece lens

focus

objective lens

stage: the slide sits on here

mirror: sends the light up through the slide

condenser: controls how much light goes up through the slide

base

Did you know?

Another Dutchman, Nicholas Hartsoeker, thought he could see tiny babies in the heads of sperm cells. Unfortunately many people believed him!

A few years later, a British scientist called Robert Hooke changed the design of the microscope. He added another lens to make objects look even bigger. This was called a **compound microscope**. Using this microscope, Hooke saw tiny compartments in a piece of cork. He thought they looked like tiny rooms and called them **cells**. The photo opposite shows a modern compound microscope.

A compound microscope is also called a **light microscope** because it uses light to let you see things.

What can you see through a microscope?

A microscope shows that your skin is made of cells.

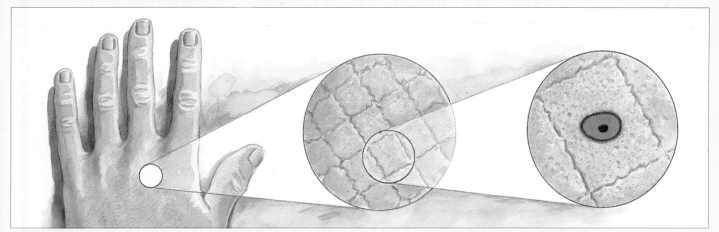

What you can see depends on the **magnification**, or how big the microscope makes things look. The lenses can be changed to give different magnifications. To work out the total magnification you multiply the power of the eyepiece lens by the power of the objective lens.

a What is the total magnification in a microscope that has an eyepiece lens of ×10 and an objective lens of ×4?

b Think about a microscope that has a choice of lenses. There are two eyepiece lenses of ×10 and ×6 and three objective lenses of ×4, ×10 and ×40. What is the maximum magnification you could get?

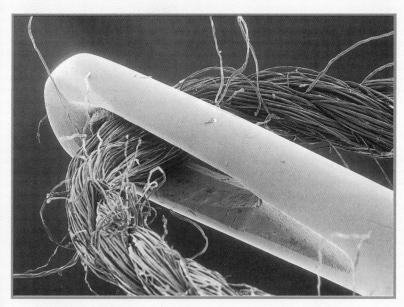

The electron microscope

In 1932, a German engineer called Ernst Ruska built the first **electron microscope**. This showed a much more detailed picture than a compound microscope. It uses electrons instead of light. Instead of looking into an eyepiece, a TV screen shows the image. The photo shows a needle and thread seen through an electron microscope.

The first electron microscope could only magnify 40 times. Modern microscopes can make an image 500 000 times larger! This allows us to see really small parts inside a cell, and find out much more about how a cell works.

Questions

1. Describe what the following parts of a microscope do:

   a stage   **b** lens   **c** condenser   **d** mirror.

2. Draw a time line to show the development of the microscope.

3. Imagine you are Robert Hooke. Write a letter to a friend explaining why your microscope is so important to scientists.

4. What do you think would be interesting to look at with an electron microscope? (Don't just think about biology.)

Types of cell

We are going to look more closely at cells. Scientists have discovered what cells look like inside, and how they work, using the electron microscope.

The house in the photo is built from thousands of bricks. In the same way, all living things are made up of tiny building blocks, called **cells**. A cell is so small that we can only see it with a microscope. We say that cells are **microscopic**.

There are two main types of cell: **animal cells** and **plant cells**. They have a lot in common, but they also have some differences.

Learn about

➤ Animal cells

➤ Plant cells

Animal cells

An animal cell is shown opposite. Surrounding the cell is a thin **cell membrane**. The membrane lets substances such as water and gases in and out of the cell. Inside the cell is a jelly-like substance called **cytoplasm**. This is where chemical changes happen to keep the cell alive. Every cell has a **nucleus**, which controls everything that happens inside the cell.

(a) Why do you think the cell membrane is important?

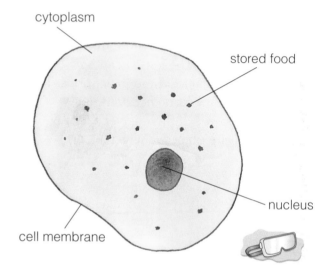

cytoplasm

stored food

nucleus

cell membrane

Plant cells

A plant cell is shown on the left. It has a cell membrane, a nucleus and cytoplasm, just as animal cells do.

Plant cells also have some parts that animal cells don't have. Plant cells have lots of small structures called **chloroplasts**. These contain a green substance called **chlorophyll**. This is why plants look green. Plants make their food in these chloroplasts.

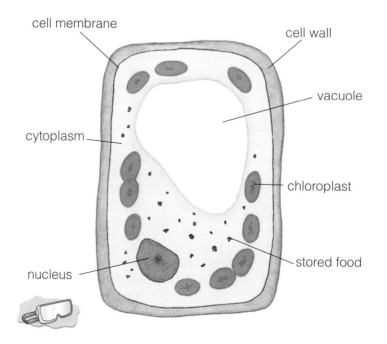

cell membrane

cell wall

cytoplasm

vacuole

chloroplast

nucleus

stored food

Every plant cell has a **cell wall** made of a tough, stringy substance called **cellulose**. This supports the cell and makes it strong. The photo below shows cellulose seen with an electron microscope.

Inside the cell is a **vacuole**. This contains a liquid called sap that keeps the cell firm.

Did you know?

The tough cell wall makes plant cells very difficult to digest. Some plants, such as celery, are so tough that you use more energy breaking down the cells than you get from eating it.

Cell shapes

Photo **A** shows human cheek cells (animal cells). Photo **B** shows onion cells (plant cells). To show up the parts inside these cells, a substance called a **stain** has been used. Without a stain, it would be very difficult to see some of the things inside the cell.

Look at the difference in shape. Animal cells have an **irregular shape** and plant cells have a **regular shape**. The strong cell wall gives plant cells their regular shape.

b Write down three differences between the two types of cell.

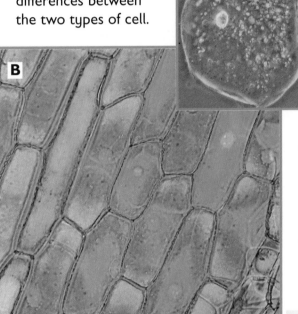

Questions

1. **a** Make a list of things that are similar in animal and plant cells.

   b Make another list of the differences between them.

2. Which part of a cell carries out each function below?

   a controls the cell

   b gives the cell shape

   c keeps the cell firm

   d carries out photosynthesis

   e controls movement into and out of the cell

   f place where chemical changes happen

3. Make a poster to describe the structure of plant and animal cells.

For your notes

All living things are made of **cells**.

There are two types of cell: **animal cells** and **plant cells**.

Both types of cell have a **cell membrane**, **cytoplasm** and a **nucleus**.

Plant cells also have a **regular shape**, a **cell wall**, **chloroplasts** and a **vacuole**.

Making food

> **a** Plants do not eat food, so where do they get their food?

The photo shows a plant in the jungle.

> **b** What do you think the plant needs so it can grow?

Plants make their own food in their leaves. This is called **photosynthesis**. It happens in the chloroplasts, which are mainly in leaf cells.

Plants take in carbon dioxide from the air and water from the soil. In photosynthesis, they use light energy from the Sun to turn these substances into food. They make sugars such as glucose. Plants also make oxygen during photosynthesis.

I love the Sun

Chloroplasts contain a green substance called **chlorophyll**. Chlorophyll absorbs the light energy needed in photosynthesis. Look at the diagram below which shows how photosynthesis happens.

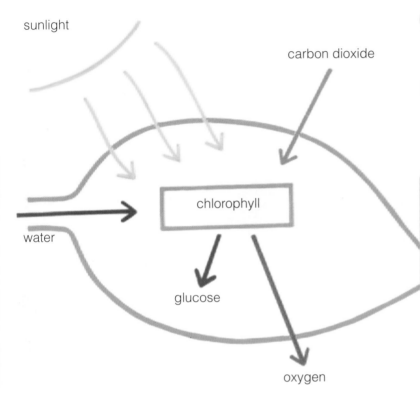

sunlight

carbon dioxide

chlorophyll

water

glucose

oxygen

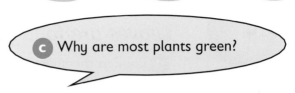

c Why are most plants green?

We can show photosynthesis as a word equation:

carbon dioxide + water → sugar + oxygen

d What gas is made in photosynthesis?

Did you know?

In the eighteenth century, the Dutch scientist Jan Ingenhousz was the first to discover that plants take in carbon dioxide and release oxygen when sunlight shines on them.

What happens to the sugars?

The plant uses the sugars it makes to grow. Sometimes the plant will turn glucose into a substance called starch to store it. You can test a leaf to see whether starch is in it. If the leaf contains starch, then the plant has been making food by photosynthesis.

Questions

1. Copy and complete these sentences.

   Photosynthesis uses _____ and _____ to make sugars.

   The green pigment in plants is called _____.

   The gas made in photosynthesis is _____.

2. Describe what would happen to photosynthesis if a plant was kept in the following conditions:

   a in the dark for a few days

   b without any carbon dioxide.

   Explain your answers.

3. What does a plant use sugars for?

4. How does the plant store food?

For your notes

Plants make food by a process called **photosynthesis**.

In photosynthesis, plants use light energy, carbon dioxide and water to make sugars and oxygen.

83

Leaf structure

Leaves are food factories

a Look at the photo below and say what these leaves have in common.

Learn about

➤ Leaf structure

➤ Photosynthesis

Most leaves are broad and flat. They have a large surface area so that they can trap as much sunlight as possible. Most leaves are green, because they contain chlorophyll. Some plants have leaves that are partly green and partly other colours. If there isn't enough light, these leaves may turn completely green to get more light energy.

Did you know?

Some plants can move their leaves so that they face the Sun all day.

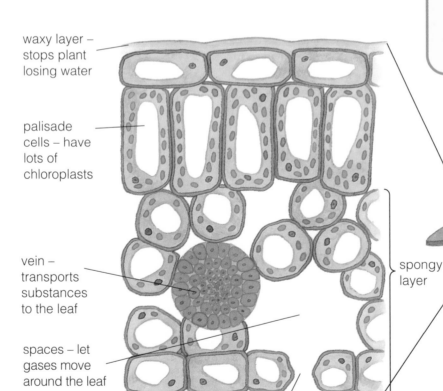

waxy layer – stops plant losing water

palisade cells – have lots of chloroplasts

vein – transports substances to the leaf

spaces – let gases move around the leaf

spongy layer

hole – lets gases in and out

The diagram on the left shows a slice through a leaf as seen through a microscope.

As well as light energy, plants need carbon dioxide and water to make their food. A leaf is adapted to get these three things and then use them to make sugars by photosynthesis. The diagram above shows the parts of the leaf and their functions.

Getting gases in and out

Look carefully at the diagram opposite of a hole in the underside of a leaf. These holes are called **stomata**. The carbon dioxide needed for photosynthesis gets into the leaves through the stomata. The oxygen made during photosynthesis moves out of the palisade cells and into the spaces of the spongy layer. The oxygen then leaves the leaf through the stomata.

Trapping light energy

The **palisade cell** is the part of the leaf where most of the food is made. Palisade cells have lots of chloroplasts containing chlorophyll, so they can trap a lot of light energy. They are close to the top surface of the leaf so that they get plenty of sunlight. The photo shows a palisade cell seen under a microscope.

b How does:
i carbon dioxide
ii water
get to the palisade cell?

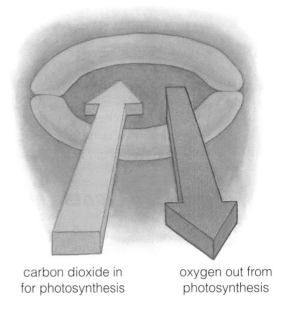

carbon dioxide in for photosynthesis

oxygen out from photosynthesis

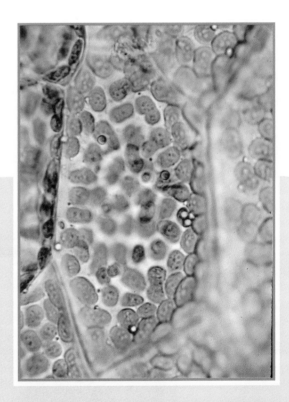

Questions

1. Write out each part of the leaf along with its correct job.

Parts of leaf	Jobs
waxy layer	transports substances to the leaf
palisade cell	allow gases into and out of the leaf
stomata	photosynthesis happens here
vein	stops water being lost

2. Think carefully about the parts of a leaf.
   a Why do palisade cells have many chloroplasts?
   b Why are the palisade cells at the top of the leaf, and not at the bottom?
   c How does the shape of the leaf help with photosynthesis?

3. Oxygen is made during photosynthesis. Why do you think this makes plants very important to humans?

For your notes

The plant makes its food by photosynthesis in the leaves.

Leaves have a large surface area to trap as much sunlight as possible.

Leaves have **stomata** so gases can move in and out.

85

The root of the problem

Plants need water

Plants need water to carry out photosynthesis. Water is transported into the leaves. Once the leaves have made food, water transports the food to where it is needed in the plant. Plants also need water to keep the cells firm and keep the plant upright. Some parts of plants are almost entirely water. A ripe tomato is about 95% water.

How plants get their water

a Look at the photo below. The roots are bigger than the part of the plant above the soil. Why do you think this is?

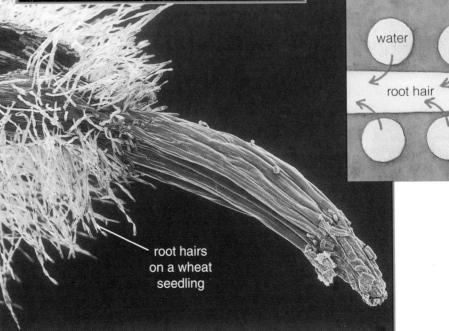

root hairs on a wheat seedling

Learn about

► The function of roots

► Root hairs

Did you know?

A wild fig tree in South Africa had roots that grew 120 metres deep.

The roots of a plant can become very large as they grow to reach water. The root has two major functions:

● taking in water

● anchoring the plant in the soil.

Roots get thinner and thinner as they spread out. The very tips of roots have many tiny parts called **root hairs**. Root hairs are long and thin. They have a large surface area to absorb water from the soil.

water

root hair

Getting water to all the parts of the plant

Water is transported through **veins** from the roots, up the stem to the leaves. Water is used in the leaves for photosynthesis. The food made in the leaves is then transported through the veins to the parts of the plant where it is needed. The food is transported as sugars dissolved in water.

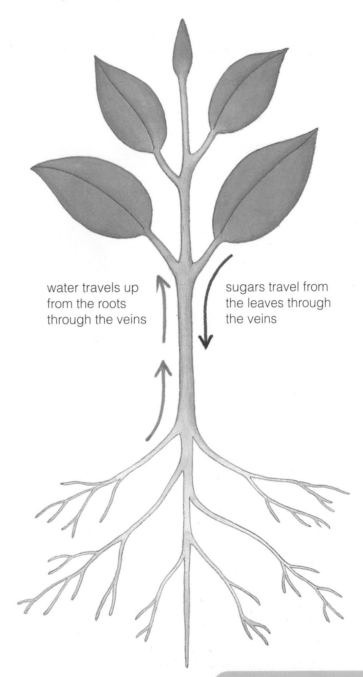

water travels up from the roots through the veins

sugars travel from the leaves through the veins

Did you know?

Hydroponics is growing plants without any soil. They grow in a liquid which gives them all they need to grow.

Did you know?

Florists stand white flowers in water with dye added. The dye travels up the veins and colours the flowers.

Questions

1. Give three reasons why plants need water.

2. What are the two main functions of a plant's roots?

3. How do root hairs help the plant take in water?

4. Write a poem or a rap describing how water and sugars are transported in a plant.

For your notes

The roots of a plant anchor it in the ground, and absorb water.

Root hairs are tiny parts with a large surface area to absorb water.

Water is transported around the plant through the **veins**.

Flowers

Flowers give great pleasure to people. William Wordsworth wrote a poem about their beauty.

> I wandered lonely as a cloud
>
> That floats on high o'er vales and hills
>
> When all at once I saw a crowd,
>
> A host of golden daffodils.

But this is not the reason why flowers exist.

(a) Why do you think a plant produces flowers?

Flowering plants reproduce by making seeds in the flowers. The seeds then grow into new plants. The male parts of a flower are the **stamens**. Each stamen is made of an **anther** and a **filament**. The female parts are the **carpels**. Each carpel is made of a **stigma**, a **style** and an **ovary**.

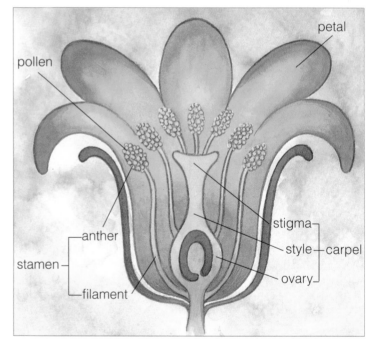

Sex cells in flowers

The male and female sex cells are found in flowers. The male sex cells are the **pollen grains**. Some pollen grains are shown in the photo, seen under a microscope. The female sex cell is the **egg cell**. Some flowers contain just male sex cells, others just female sex cells. Most flowers contain both.

Pollination

Pollination is the transfer of pollen grains from an anther to a stigma. It may happen when an insect such as a bee goes from flower to flower. Pollen sticks to the bee and gets carried from one flower to the next. Pollination can also happen when wind blows pollen about.

b Describe how a bee, called Polly Nation, helps with pollination.

Fertilisation

Fertilisation happens when the nucleus of the male sex cell joins with the nucleus of the female sex cell. In plants, fertilisation happens after pollination. The nucleus of the pollen grain and the nucleus of the egg cell join to produce a fertilised egg cell. The picture on the right shows how it happens.

What happens to the fertilised egg cell?

The new fertilised egg cell grows to form an **embryo plant**. The ovule forms a **seed** with the embryo plant inside it. The seed protects the embryo plant and contains a food store for the tiny plant. The ovary forms the **fruit** with the seed inside it.

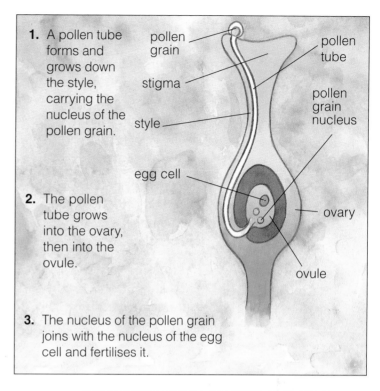

1. A pollen tube forms and grows down the style, carrying the nucleus of the pollen grain.

2. The pollen tube grows into the ovary, then into the ovule.

3. The nucleus of the pollen grain joins with the nucleus of the egg cell and fertilises it.

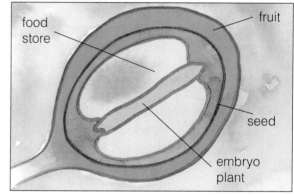

Questions

1. Write out each part of a flower along with its correct function.

Flower parts	Functions
stigma	receives the pollen grains
carpel	male part of a flower
anther	female part of a flower
stamen	makes the pollen grains

2. Draw a flow diagram to show how seeds are formed. Include the following words:

   > **stamens   pollen grain   carpel   egg cell**
   > **pollination   pollen tube   fertilisation**
   > **embryo plant   bee**

For your notes

Flowers contain the sex parts of the plant.

The male sex cells are the **pollen grains**.

The female sex cells are the **egg cells**.

Pollination is the transfer of the pollen grains from the **anther** to the **stigma**.

Fertilisation happens when the nucleus of the pollen grain joins with the nucleus of an egg cell.

Scaling up and down

Too small to see

A cell is smaller than the end of a pencil, so it is impossible to draw a cell at its real size. We need to draw it much larger than it really is. Scientists call this a **scale diagram**.

Scale diagrams are also useful for showing things that are too big to fit on a page. We draw big things smaller than they really are. Maps are scale diagrams.

a Discuss in your group other uses for scale diagrams.

Scales

Scaling up means showing an object bigger than it really is. A microscope scales things up. **Scaling down** means showing an object smaller than it really is.

The picture shows Mr and Mrs Beetroot with their two children Nick and Aileen. They are not really this small. They have been scaled down. To find out how big they really are, we have to scale up again.

Mr Beetroot   Mrs Beetroot   Nick   Aileen

In this picture, 1 cm is used to show 40 cm in real life. In the picture Mr Beetroot is 5 cm tall. To find his real height you multiply his height in the picture by 40. This means you scale up by 40:

5 × 40 = 200
So Mr Beetroot
is 200 cm tall.

Instead of using lots of words to describe scaling up, we can say the **scale factor** for the picture is 40. This means you multiply by 40. So 1 cm represents 40 cm.

b Copy and complete the table to find the real heights of the rest of the Beetroot family.

Name	Picture height in cm	Scale factor	Picture height × scale factor	Real height in cm
Mr Beetroot	5	40	5 × 40	200
Mrs Beetroot	4	40		
Nick	3	40		
Aileen	2	40		

When we want to scale up, we multiply by a scale factor. Now imagine we want to scale down.

c Discuss in your group how you think we can scale down using the scale factor.

If you want Mr Beetroot scaled down by a factor of 20, you divide his real height by 20.

> 200 ÷ 20 = 10 cm. So you would draw Mr Beetroot 10 cm tall.

d Draw a table with these headings and work out how tall you would draw the rest of the Beetroot family.

Name	Real height in cm	Scale factor	Real height ÷ scale factor	Picture height in cm
Mr Beetroot	200	**20**	200 ÷ 20	**10**

Finding the scale factor

If you know the real size and the picture size of something, then you can find the scale factor using the formula:

$$\text{scale factor} = \frac{\text{real size}}{\text{picture size}}$$

e Nick has to find the scale factor for a number of household objects. Copy and complete Nick's table shown below.

Object	Real height in cm	Picture height in cm	Real height ÷ picture height	Scale factor
Science book	30	**3**		
House	800	**40**		
TV	60	**12**		

Questions

1. Aileen drew her doll 5 cm high. Its real height is 50 cm. Find the scale factor she used to draw the picture.

2. The following table lists some of the objects in the Beetroots' house. Copy and complete the table.

Object	Real measurement in cm	Picture measurement in cm	Scale factor
Length of car	300	**10**	
Length of pencil		**2**	10
Width of garden	600		50

3. Measure your height in centimetres. Work out how you could draw a scale diagram to represent your height. Draw a line to show your height scaled down by a factor of 10.

Metals through the ages

Metals 7.1

Historic metals

Metals are very important in our lives. They were also very important in the lives of people throughout history.

The pictures below show the types of metals people have used over the last 7000 years. People use different metals for different things.

Setting the scene

Look at the pictures.

b Which people first started to use iron to make weapons?

d Who invented a way of making large amounts of cheap steel?

Before 5000 BC Stone Age people found pieces of gold in rivers.

3000 BC Egyptians used gold, silver, copper and bronze.

1200 BC Hittites made wrought iron from rocks.

500 BC Small pieces of steel were made from wrought iron.

300 BC The Chinese invented cast iron. It was not used in Europe for 1100 years.

1665 AD Dud Dudley started to make cast iron using coke instead of charcoal.

1856 AD Henry Bessemer made large amounts of cheap steel.

Using metals

Gold and silver are used for jewellery. Steel is used to make bridges and large buildings. How a metal is used depends on:

- how it behaves. We call this the metal's **properties**.
- how easy it is to make.

Very few metals as found as metals. Most metals are found as rocks called **ores**. The ore is mined from the ground. The useful parts are separated and changed into the metal by a chemical reaction.

Did you know?

In 688 AD the Chinese built a pagoda of cast iron that was 90 m tall.

Look at the fact files on the opposite page.

e Bronze is a mixture of copper and tin. How does copper change when it is made into bronze?

f How does mixing iron with different amounts of carbon change its properties?

Fact files

Gold

- yellow, very soft, very flexible
- found as gold, so very easy to use
- very rare

Bronze (80% copper, 20% tin)

- brown, hard, brittle
- copper and tin are found as rocks and are changed into metals
- the metals are melted together and mixed

Copper

- pink, soft, flexible
- found as a rock and changed into copper (by heating with carbon)
- more common than gold

Wrought iron (iron with less than 0.1% carbon)

- grey, soft, flexible
- found as a rock
- the rock is heated with carbon to make the metal
- the metal is beaten with a hammer

Cast iron (iron with about 3% carbon)

- grey, hard, brittle
- found as a rock
- the rock is heated with carbon to a very high temperature

Steel (iron with 0.5%–2.0% carbon)
- grey, hard, flexible
- found as a rock
- made from cast iron by heating again and burning off some of the carbon

Questions

1. Draw a time line to show these events in the order in which they happened.

> making wrought iron
> making cast iron
> making bronze
> making large amounts of steel
> making small amounts of steel
> making copper
> finding gold

2. Look back at the pictures on the opposite page. The Hittites were the first people to use iron for knives. Imagine you are a Hittite blacksmith. You have started to make iron knives, but your customers want to buy the bronze knives they are used to.

   Write a story about how you persuade your customers to buy iron knives. Use the fact files for wrought iron and bronze to help you.

3. Copy the table below. Use the information on these pages to complete it.

	Steel	Copper	Bronze	Wrought iron	Cast iron
Is it found as the metal or as a rock?					
Can you bend it?					
Is it hard?					

What is a metal?

Properties

The **properties** of a material show how it behaves. Properties include the temperature it melts at (**melting point**), the temperature it boils at (**boiling point**), whether it conducts thermal energy and whether it conducts electricity.

Metals conduct electricity

You can use metals to complete a circuit because they let electricity pass through them. We say metals **conduct electricity**. Most wires are made of copper. Some wires, like the ones in the element of a toaster, are made of nichrome. This is a mixture of nickel and chromium. The cables between electricity pylons are made of aluminium. The prongs on most plugs are made of brass. Brass is a mixture of copper and zinc.

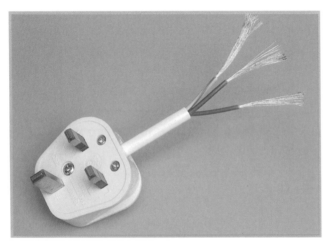

Metals conduct thermal energy

We make saucepans of copper, cast iron, stainless steel and aluminium because metals let thermal energy pass easily. We say that metals **conduct thermal energy**.

Learn about

➤ The properties of metals

Metals are shiny

Some metals are magnetic

Iron is **magnetic**, and so are nickel and cobalt. These metals are attracted to a magnet. Steel will also stick to a magnet, because steel contains iron.

a How could you separate aluminium cans from steel cans?

Most metals are solids

We are comfortable living at 25 °C. Look at the chart opposite. The dotted line shows 25 °C.

b Which metal is a liquid at 25 °C?

c Which metal would melt if heated from 25 °C to 100 °C?

d Which metal would not melt in the hottest part of a Bunsen burner flame?

e Which three metals would boil in the hottest part of a Bunsen burner flame?

f Many thermometers contain mercury. Mercury thermometers can only be used between −60 °C and 350 °C. Use the information in the chart to explain why.

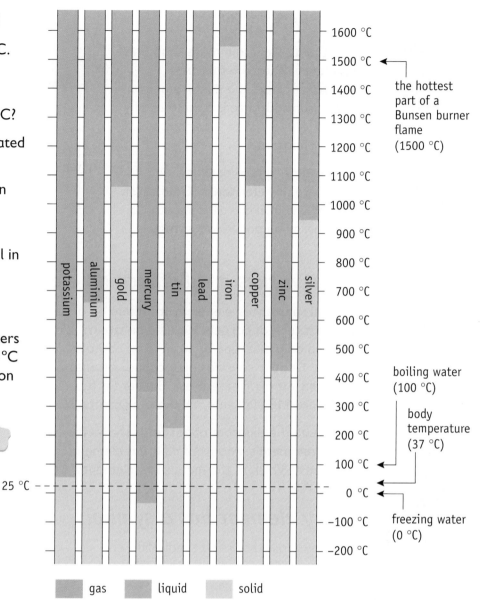

the hottest part of a Bunsen burner flame (1500 °C)

boiling water (100 °C)

body temperature (37 °C)

freezing water (0 °C)

gas   liquid   solid

Questions

1. Make a list, in alphabetical order, of all the metals mentioned on these two pages. Add any other metals mentioned on the previous two pages. Which of these metals are mixtures of two or more substances?

2. Use the information in the table below to make your own chart like the one above.

Metal	Melting point in °C	Boiling point in °C
Sodium	98	883
Magnesium	649	1107
Nickel	1455	2730

For your notes

Metals are shiny.

Metals are good **conductors of electricity** and **thermal energy**.

A few metals, including iron, are **magnetic**.

Most metals are solids at room temperature.

Metals as elements

Elements

Some metals contain more than one substance. These metals are **mixtures**. Steel is a mixture of iron and carbon. Bronze is a mixture of copper and tin. Brass is a mixture of copper and zinc.

Metals that contain only one substance are **elements**. Gold, silver, copper and iron are all elements. So are zinc, nickel and 90 other metals.

Learn about

➤ Elements

Did you know?

Leucippus was born about 490 BC. As far as we know, he was the first person to suggest that everything was made up of little bits. The idea was taken further by his student Democritus. He thought that these little bits could not be split up, so he called them **atoms**. The Greek word *atomos* means 'cannot be divided'.

What makes a substance an element?

Like all substances, elements are made up of particles. The simplest type of particle is called an **atom**. Elements contain only one type of atom. Iron contains only iron atoms. Copper contains only copper atoms. Zinc contains only zinc atoms. There are 118 different types of atom, so there are 118 elements. Of these elements, 96 are metals.

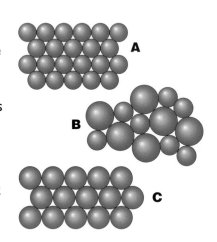

a Study the diagram opposite. It shows the atoms in three metals. Atoms of different elements are different sizes. Which of the metals are elements?

Every element has a symbol

People across the world speak different languages. The word for iron is different in each language. However, scientists across the world use the same **symbol** for iron. Each element has a symbol that scientists everywhere use.

There are some rules for symbols:

● the first letter is a capital letter

● if there are second and third letters, they are small letters.

b Imagine that each symbol was only one letter. How many different symbols could there be? Would this be enough?

Some elements have been known from ancient times. The symbol for iron, Fe, comes from the Latin word for iron (*ferrum*). Latin was the language spoken by the Romans. Gold has the symbol Au, from the Latin word for gold (*aurum*). Silver has the symbol Ag, from the Latin word for silver (*argentum*). Tungsten has the symbol W, from the German word for tungsten (*wolfram*).

c Caesium, calcium, chromium, cobalt, copper, cadmium, cerium, curium and californium are all metallic elements starting with C. Which symbol below goes with which element? (Hint: the Latin name for copper was *cuprum*.)

Cm Cs Cu Cd Cf Cr Ca Co Ce

Putting the elements in order

Learning about the 118 elements takes a long time, so we put them in a special table to make it easier. This table is called the **periodic table**, and most of it is shown below. It is used by scientists all over the world.

d Where are the metals in the periodic table? Are they to the left or to the right as you look at the table?

metals

non-metals

H

I	II	←			Groups						→	III	IV	V	VI	VII	0	Periods
																	He	1
Li	Be											B	C	N	O	F	Ne	2
Na	Mg											Al	Si	P	S	Cl	Ar	3
K	Ca	Sc	Ti	V	Cr	Mn	Fe	Co	Ni	Cu	Zn	Ga	Ge	As	Se	Br	Kr	4
Rb	Sr	Y	Zr	Nb	Mo	Tc	Ru	Rh	Pd	Ag	Cd	In	Sn	Sb	Te	I	Xe	5
Cs	Ba	Lu	Hf	Ta	W	Re	Os	Ir	Pt	Au	Hg	Tl	Pb	Bi	Po	At	Rn	6
Fr	Ra	Lr	Rf	Db	Sg	Bh	Hs	Mt	Uun	Uuu	Uub		Uuq		Uuh		Uuo	7

The vertical columns in the periodic table are called **groups**. The elements in a group are alike. The horizontal rows are called **periods**.

Questions

1. Brass is a mixture. Copper is an element. Explain why copper is an element and why brass is not an element.

2. Lillian thinks that the element F is a metal. Sarah looks at the periodic table and says it is not a metal. Who do you think is right, and why?

3. Joe thinks that all elements should have the first letter of their name as their symbol. Copper should be C and silver should be S. Do you think Joe is right? Give reasons for your answer.

For your notes

We call the simplest type of particle an **atom**.

An **element** is a substance with only one type of atom.

Many metals are elements.

Each element has a **symbol**.

We arrange the elements in the **periodic table**.

The periodic table has **groups** (columns) and **periods** (rows).

Some more elements

We have seen that most metals are solids. Metals are shiny, and they conduct electricity and thermal energy.

Look at the fact files for some gases here.

a Do you think these elements are metals? Give four reasons for your answer.

b Look back to the periodic table on page 97. Are these elements to the right or to the left of the table?

Fact files: some gases

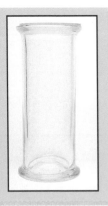

Element: Oxygen

Symbol: O
State at 25 °C: gas
Colour: colourless
Conduct electricity? ✗
Conduct
thermal energy?   ✗

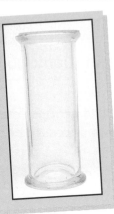

Element: Nitrogen

Symbol: N
State at 25 °C: gas
Colour: colourless
Conduct electricity? ✗
Conduct
thermal energy?   ✗

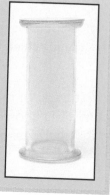

Element: Chlorine

Symbol: Cl
State at 25 °C: gas
Colour: green
Conduct electricity? ✗
Conduct
thermal energy?   ✗

Learn about

➤ Non-metals

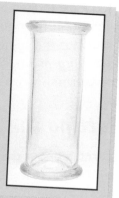

Element: Hydrogen

Symbol: H
State at 25 °C: gas
Colour: colourless
Conduct electricity? ✗
Conduct
thermal energy?   ✗

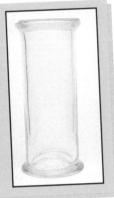

Element: Helium

Symbol: He
State at 25 °C: gas
Colour: colourless
Conduct electricity? ✗
Conduct
thermal energy?   ✗

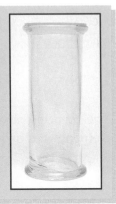

Element: Fluorine

Symbol: F
State at 25 °C: gas
Colour: yellow
Conduct electricity? ✗
Conduct
thermal energy?   ✗

Look at the fact files for some solids and liquids on the opposite page.

c Do you think that the following elements are metals? Give reasons for your answers.

i bromine   **ii** sulphur   **iii** carbon

d Look back at the periodic table. In which part of the table are the elements in question **c** found?

Fact files: some solids and liquids

Element: Bromine

Symbol: Br
State at 25 °C: liquid
Colour: red
Conduct electricity? ✗
Conduct thermal energy? ✗

Element: Sulphur

Symbol: S
State at 25 °C: solid
Colour: yellow
Conduct electricity? ✗
Conduct thermal energy? ✗

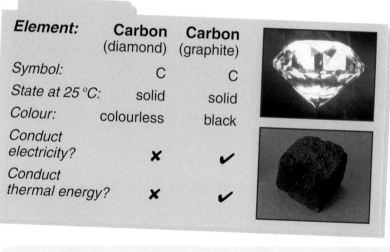

Element:	Carbon (diamond)	Carbon (graphite)
Symbol:	C	C
State at 25 °C:	solid	solid
Colour:	colourless	black
Conduct electricity?	✗	✔
Conduct thermal energy?	✗	✔

Non-metal elements

The elements in the fact files on these two pages are **non-metals**. Unlike metals, most non-metals are not shiny solids. They do not conduct electricity or thermal energy very well. There are lots of non-metals with different properties. Some of them are solids, and some are liquids. Many of them are gases.

Some of these gases are very useful. Oxygen is used to keep premature babies alive. Chlorine is used to kill bacteria in water treatment plants. Helium is a gas that is lighter than air, so balloons filled with helium float. Hydrogen is another useful element which is a gas. It can be used as a fuel.

e What is chlorine used for?

Questions

1. Name an element that is:
   a a non-metal and a liquid
   b a non-metal and a green gas
   c a non-metal and a yellow solid
   d a non-metal and a gas we need to live.

2. In what three ways are most non-metals different from most metals?

3. Carbon comes in two forms: graphite and diamond.
   a Which form is a typical non-metal? Give your reasons.
   b Which form has some properties of metals and some of non-metals? Explain your answer.

For your notes

Some elements are **non-metals**.

Most non-metals are not shiny.

Most non-metals do not conduct electricity.

Most non-metals do not conduct thermal energy.

Some non-metals are solids, some are liquids and some are gases at room temperature.

Getting it right

Metal or non-metal?

Scientists have used the properties of metals to decide that:

- iron, copper, nickel and mercury are metals
- carbon, sulphur, selenium, bromine and chlorine are non-metals.

Joe's class want to put these nine elements into two groups, metals and non-metals. There are fact files about the nine elements on the opposite page.

Lillian's idea

Put all the solids in one group. Metals are solids. All the others will be non-metals.

a i Which elements will be in Lillian's 'metals' group?

ii Which elements will be in Lillian's 'non-metals' group?

iii Is Lillian's idea going to work? Explain your answer.

Joe's idea

Test the elements with a magnet. The ones that stick to the magnet are metals. The others are non-metals.

b i Which elements will be in Joe's 'metals' group?

ii Which elements will be in Joe's 'non-metals' group?

iii Is Joe's idea going to work? Explain your answer.

Yasmin's idea

See which elements conduct electricity. The ones that do are metals, the others are non-metals.

c i Which elements will be in Yasmin's 'metals' group?

ii Which elements will be in Yasmin's 'non-metals' group?

iii Is Yasmin's idea going to work? Explain your answer.

Tony's idea

The shiny ones are metals. All the others are non-metals.

d i Which elements will be in Tony's 'metals' group?

ii Which elements will be in Tony's 'non-metals' group?

iii Is Tony's idea going to work? Explain your answer.

e Which were the most successful of the four ideas?

f Decide on two questions that will group the elements into metals and non-metals.

Fact files

The metals are in yellow boxes. The non-metals are in pink boxes.

Element: Copper

Symbol:	Cu
State at 25 °C:	solid
Colour:	pink
Shiny?	✔
Magnetic?	✘
Conduct electricity?	✔
Conduct thermal energy?	✔

Element: Mercury

Symbol:	Hg
State at 25 °C:	liquid
Colour:	silver
Shiny?	✔
Magnetic?	✘
Conduct electricity?	✔
Conduct thermal energy?	✔

Element: Iron

Symbol:	Fe
State at 25 °C:	solid
Colour:	grey
Shiny?	✔
Magnetic?	✔
Conduct electricity?	✔
Conduct thermal energy?	✔

Element: Nickel

Symbol:	Ni
State at 25 °C:	solid
Colour:	grey
Shiny?	✔
Magnetic?	✔
Conduct electricity?	✔
Conduct thermal energy?	✔

Element: Selenium

Symbol:	Se
State at 25 °C::	solid
Colour:	silver
Shiny?	✔
Magnetic?	✘
Conduct electricity?	✘
Conduct thermal energy?	✘

Element: Carbon

Symbol:	C
State at 25 °C:	solid
Colour:	black
Shiny?	✘
Magnetic?	✘
Conduct electricity?	✔
Conduct thermal energy?	✔

Element: Sulphur

Symbol:	S
State at 25 °C:	solid
Colour:	yellow
Shiny?	✘
Magnetic?	✘
Conduct electricity?	✘
Conduct thermal energy?	✘

Element: Bromine

Symbol:	Br
State at 25 °C:	liquid
Colour:	red
Shiny?	✘
Magnetic?	✘
Conduct electricity?	✘
Conduct thermal energy?	✘

Element: Chlorine

Symbol:	Cl
State at 25 °C:	gas
Colour:	green
Shiny?	✘
Magnetic?	✘
Conduct electricity?	✘
Conduct thermal energy?	✘

Questions

There are some elements that do not fit neatly into the group 'metals' or the group 'non-metals'.

1. Look at the information about silicon, phosphorus and boron in the table below. Which are metals and which are non-metals? Give reasons for your decisions.

Element	State at 25 °C	Colour	Shiny?	Magnetic?	Conduct electricity?	Conduct thermal energy?
Silicon	Solid	Grey	✔	✘	✘	✔
Phosphorus	Solid	Black	✘	✘	✔	✘
Boron	Solid	Grey	✘	✘	✘	✔

Heating metals

Melting and freezing

When you heat a metal, it melts. The solid becomes a liquid. When it cools, the liquid becomes a solid again. This is a **reversible** change. It is an example of a **physical change**. No new substances are made during a physical change.

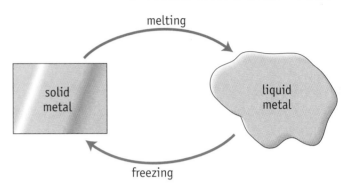

melting

solid metal

liquid metal

freezing

Look at the table of melting points opposite.

(a) Which metal is a liquid at room temperature (25 °C)?

(b) Which metal would melt if you heated it from 25 °C to body temperature (37 °C)?

(c) Which metal would melt if you heated it from 37 °C to 100 °C (the boiling point of water)?

(d) Which metal would melt if you heated it from 100 °C to 1000 °C using a Bunsen burner?

Metal	Melting point in °C
Sodium	98
Cadmium	321
Mercury	−39
Gallium	30
Titanium	1660

Making new substances

When you heat the metal magnesium in air, it burns. Light energy and thermal energy are given out. The metal is burned and a white powder is made. The white powder does not turn back into magnesium as it cools. This is an **irreversible** change.

The magnesium has reacted with oxygen. A **chemical change** or **chemical reaction** has happened. A new substance has been made. The new substance is called magnesium oxide.

(e) What would you see if you melted magnesium?

(f) How is melting magnesium different from burning magnesium?

A different gas

When you burn a metal in air, you make a metal **oxide**. The metal magnesium reacts with oxygen in the air to make magnesium oxide.

> magnesium + oxygen → magnesium oxide

g Write a word equation for the reaction of the metal lithium with oxygen.

What happens if we use a different gas instead of oxygen? If we use chlorine gas, we make a **chloride**. Sodium is a silver metal. Chlorine is a green gas. They react to make sodium chloride, a white powder. The photo opposite shows this.

> sodium + chlorine → sodium chloride

h Lithium reacts with chlorine. Write a word equation for the reaction.

A different non-metal

Oxygen and chlorine are both non-metals. Metals will also react with other non-metals.

Look at the photo opposite. When iron is heated with sulphur, it starts to glow. The chemical reaction gives out light energy and thermal energy, like burning the magnesium. Iron **sulphide** is made.

> iron + sulphur → iron sulphide

i Write a word equation for the reaction between zinc and sulphur.

Questions

1. Write word equations for these reactions.

   a potassium with chlorine

   b aluminium with oxygen

   c calcium with sulphur

2. Study the list of changes below. List the ones that are physical changes (that can easily be reversed).

   > **melting ice   a match burning
   > baking a cake   boiling water
   > dissolving sugar   iron rusting**

3. New substances are made during a chemical reaction. Kim is carrying out different chemical reactions. What might she see that tells her new substances have been made?

4. Fluorine is another non-metal. Suggest what substance will be made when magnesium reacts with fluorine.

For your notes

No new substances are made during a **physical change**. New substances are made in a **chemical reaction**.

An **oxide** is made when a metal reacts with oxygen.

A **chloride** is made when a metal reacts with chlorine.

A **sulphide** is made when a metal reacts with sulphur.

Building bridges

When we leave iron outside, it changes. The shiny, hard metal turns into the brown, crumbly substance that we call **rust**. Scientists call rust **iron oxide**.

A bridge made of rust is not strong enough to carry lorries. You can put your finger through the door of a very rusty car. A very rusty ship will develop holes and sink. If we let something get rusty it will no longer do its job. We will have to replace it. We need to understand rusting so we can stop it happening.

Other metals also change when they are left outside for a long time. We call this process **corrosion**. Many metals corrode, but only iron rusts.

(a) What happens to the iron as a car rusts?

What makes iron rust?

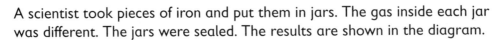

A scientist took pieces of iron and put them in jars. The gas inside each jar was different. The jars were sealed. The results are shown in the diagram.

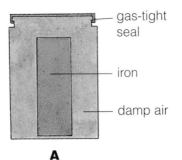

gas-tight seal

iron

damp air

A

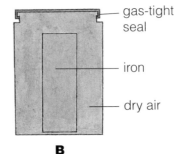

gas-tight seal

iron

dry air

B

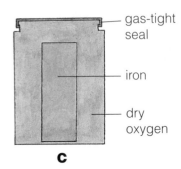

gas-tight seal

iron

dry oxygen

C

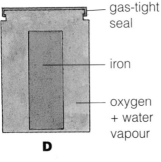

gas-tight seal

iron

oxygen + water vapour

D

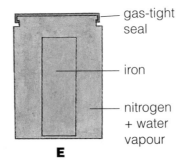

gas-tight seal

iron

nitrogen + water vapour

E

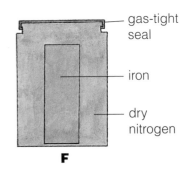

gas-tight seal

iron

dry nitrogen

F

(b) Which pieces of iron went rusty?

(c) Which jars contained oxygen?

(d) Which jars contained water?

(e) Which jars contained both oxygen and water?

(f) What three substances have to be present for rusting to take place?

(g) Why did the scientist include jar **F**?

Preventing rusting

Oxygen and water must both be present for iron to rust. Keeping oxygen and water away from the iron will stop it rusting.

h Oiling a bicycle chain stops it rusting. Explain why.

i Painting an iron bridge stops it rusting. Explain why.

Coating iron with tin stops it rusting. Tin does not rust as iron does. The layer of tin keeps the oxygen and water away from the iron.

Steel is mostly iron, so it rusts. However, **stainless steel** does not rust. Stainless steel is a mixture of iron, carbon and chromium. The chromium forms a layer of chromium oxide on the surface of the steel. This layer stops the oxygen and water reaching the iron.

j Explain why stainless steel cutlery does not rust.

k Why would a manufacturer make an iron bucket coated with tin rather than an iron bucket or a tin bucket? Use what you know and the extra information in the table.

Metal	Cost in £/kg
Iron	1.50
Tin	26.00

Questions

1. Is rusting a physical change or a chemical reaction? Explain your answer.

2. Study the experiment shown on the right. Say whether each nail will rust. Give reasons for your answers.

3. Many cars are sold with a 10 year guarantee against corrosion. Suggest three ways of making cars more rustproof.

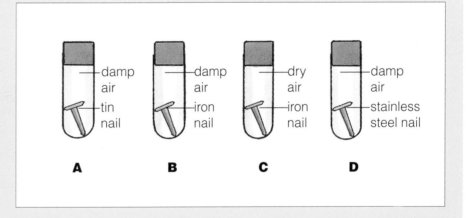

A — damp air — tin nail

B — damp air — iron nail

C — dry air — iron nail

D — damp air — stainless steel nail

For your notes

Iron **rusts** when oxygen and water can get to it.

Rusting turns iron into **iron oxide**.

Rusting is one type of **corrosion**. Corrosion destroys metals.

Metals

Compounds

7.8

Joinin up

Magnesium oxide is not a metal or a non-metal.
Magnesium oxide is not an element. It does not have a place in the periodic table.

Magnesium oxide is made when magnesium and oxygen react together. It contains both magnesium atoms and oxygen atoms. The magnesium atoms and the oxygen atoms have joined during the reaction. Substances that contain more than one type of atom joined together are called **compounds**.

Learn about

➤ Compounds

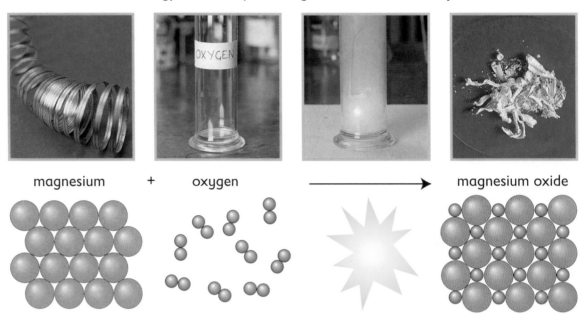

magnesium + oxygen ⟶ magnesium oxide

a Which two types of atom have joined up to make magnesium oxide?

Some compounds are solids

Magnesium oxide is a solid. The particles are close together and arranged in neat rows. All the compounds made when a metal reacts with a non-metal are solids.

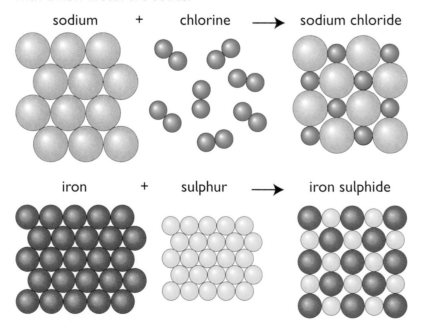

sodium + chlorine ⟶ sodium chloride

iron + sulphur ⟶ iron sulphide

Look at the diagrams of oxygen and chlorine. Both gases contain groups of atoms called **molecules**.

b How many chlorine atoms are there in a chlorine molecule?

c Count the iron particles and the sulphur particles in the iron sulphide. What is the ratio of iron to sulphur particles?

Some compounds are liquids or gases

Not all compounds are solids. Water is a compound, and it is made up of molecules. Each water molecule has one oxygen atom and two hydrogen atoms. Water is a liquid at room temperature.

Carbon dioxide is also a compound. Carbon dioxide contains carbon and oxygen atoms joined together in molecules. Carbon dioxide is a gas at room temperature.

d One water molecule contains one oxygen atom and two hydrogen atoms. How many water molecules are in the diagram opposite?

e What is the ratio of carbon atoms to oxygen atoms in carbon dioxide?

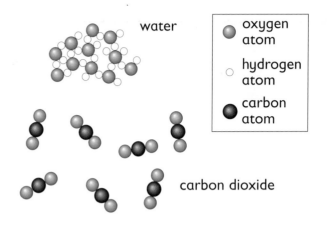

water

oxygen atom

hydrogen atom

carbon atom

carbon dioxide

Did you know?

The pictures of atoms on these pages are 25 million times bigger than the real atoms.

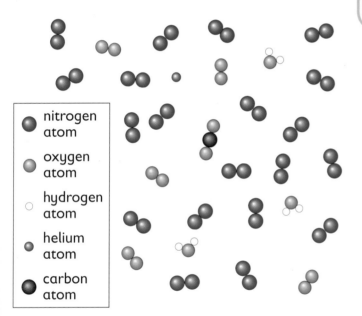

nitrogen atom

oxygen atom

hydrogen atom

helium atom

carbon atom

Mixtures, elements and compounds

The materials around us are usually **mixtures** of different substances. Some materials are mixtures of elements, for example steel contains two elements, iron and carbon. Other materials are mixtures of compounds, for example sugar solution is a mixture of two compounds, water and sugar. A material that contains only one substance is **pure**. Pure iron contains only the element iron. Pure water contains only the compound water.

Air is a mixture. The diagram opposite shows the particles in air.

Questions

Study the diagram above showing the particles in air.

1. How many different sorts of atom are there?

2. How many different substances are mixed together?

3. How many substances can you find that are elements?

4. Name the elements you have found.

5. How many substances can you find that are compounds?

6. Name the compounds you have found.

7. Explain carefully the difference between an element and a compound.

For your notes

A **compound** is a substance with more than one type of atom joined together.

A **pure** substance contains only one element or compound.

A **molecule** is a group of atoms joined together.

Forces

8.1

Sports day

Forces everywhere

Everything you do uses forces. You cannot see forces, but you can often see the effects of a force. A force can change the shape of an object, or make it move faster or slower, or make it change direction. The greater the force, the greater its effects. You can see the effects of forces in the sports day events happening on this page. 'Push' and 'pull' are two types of forces.

a What equipment could you use to measure forces?

b What units do we use to measure forces?

Throwing

Look at Sam throwing the javelin. He runs and then throws the javelin to make it go as far as possible.

c What force does Sam exert to make the javelin move, a push, a pull or both?

Running

In the race, Alex had to run hard against the strong wind. At the end of the race Alex was told how fast she ran.

d When Alex runs, what sort of force does the wind exert?

e What two things would Alex need to know to work out her speed?

Jumping

James was in the pole-vault competition. He put the long pole in the ground and jumped up. The pole bent as he jumped, and then straightened. The bendy pole helped James jump over the bar. After the jump, he fell down onto the soft mat.

f Give the names of some of the forces that help James in the pole-vault competition.

g What is the name of the force that brought James back down to the ground?

Gravity is the force that pulls everything towards the centre of the Earth. It is gravity that pulls you down when you jump in the air.

Shot-putting

On sports day Paddy threw a shot across the school field. The shot left a big dent in the grass. The grounds keeper had to do a lot of work to get it flat again.

h If the same shot weighed twice as much, what do you think would happen to the dent in the grass?

Sports day in Australia

The Earth is a sphere. Britain and Australia are almost on opposite sides.

Gravity pulls the girls downwards.

i Which way is 'downwards' in Australia?

j Why does Shirley not fall off Australia?

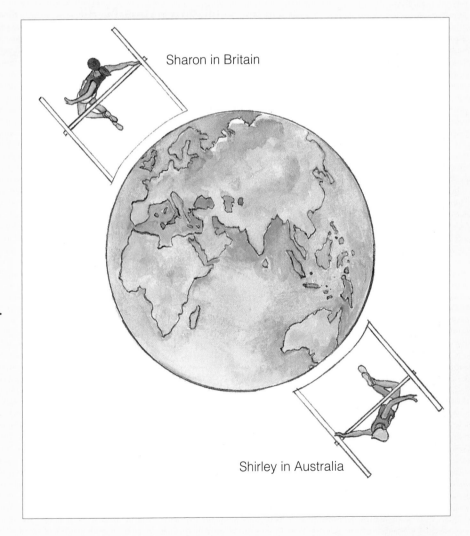

Sharon in Britain

Shirley in Australia

Questions

1. Give three effects that forces can have on objects.

2. Give three examples of how forces are useful in everyday life.

3. Give another word for the force of gravity.

Forces and gravity

What is weight?

When you pick an object up off the floor, you are lifting it against a force. This force is the object's **weight**, which pulls it down. In the picture, Samson has to pull with a force greater than the dumbbell's weight to pick up the dumbbell.

We use 'weight' to mean how heavy something is. Weight is a force that pulls things downwards. Weight is the force of gravity on an object. Heavy objects are pulled down with a bigger force than light objects. We measure weight in units called **newtons, N** All forces are measured in newtons.

What is gravity?

Gravity is the force that pulls everything towards the centre of the Earth. The Moon also has gravity pulling things towards its centre, but the Moon's gravity is weaker than the Earth's.

Samson's pull

dumbbell's weight

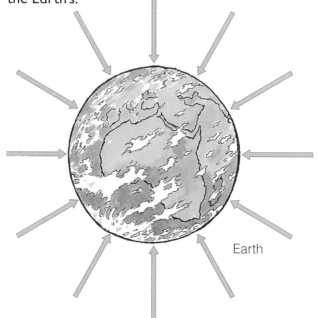

Earth

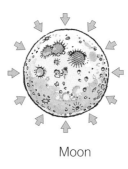

Moon

On Earth, Flo weighs about 660 N. On the Moon she weighs only 110 N. The Moon's gravity is one-sixth the strength of the Earth's gravity.

a Would you weigh more on the Earth or on the Moon?

b If you weighed 600 N on Earth, what would you weigh on the Moon?

Mass and weight

Imagine Flo goes to the Moon for lunar sports day. She is still the same size and shape as she is on Earth. She is still made of the same amount of stuff or matter. Flo's **mass** is a measure of how much matter she is made of. Mass is measured in **kilograms, kg**.

Flo's mass is the same on Earth and on the Moon. Her weight is different, because her weight is the force of gravity pulling on her mass. To find the weight of something on Earth, you multiply its mass by 10. On Earth a mass of 1 kg has a weight of 10 N. This is the **gravitational force** on Earth.

c What is the weight on Earth of an object with a mass of 8 kg?

Earth

weight 660 N
mass 66 kg

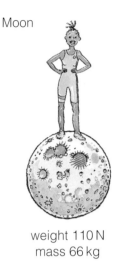

Moon

weight 110 N
mass 66 kg

On Jupiter

If you travelled further into space and held sports day on the planet Jupiter, you would find the gravity on Jupiter much stronger than on Earth.

d Gravity on Jupiter is 2.5 times as strong as on Earth. What would be the weight of a man on Jupiter if he weighs 400 N on Earth?

The gravitational force an object exerts depends on the mass of the object. The Moon has a smaller mass than the Earth. Jupiter has a bigger mass than the Earth.

The gravitational force between two objects also depends on how far apart those objects are. As a spaceship travels away from the Earth, its weight becomes smaller. Its mass stays the same but the gravitational force gets smaller as the distance from Earth increases. The picture below shows this.

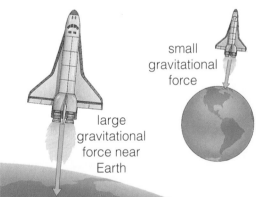

small gravitational force

large gravitational force near Earth

Questions

1. Explain what these words mean:

   a weight   **b** mass   **c** gravity.

2. Calculate the weight on Earth of the people below:

   a Susan, mass 70 kg

   b Philippa, mass 55 kg

   c Marco, mass 88 kg.

3. Flo's rabbit has a mass of 6 kg. What is the weight of the rabbit on:

   a the Earth?   **b** the Moon?   **c** Jupiter?

4. Explain how the following affect the gravitational force:

   a mass   **b** the distance between objects.

For your notes

Gravity is the force that pulls everything towards the centre of the Earth.

Weight is the force of gravity on an object. Weight is a force, measured in **newtons, N**.

Mass is a measure of how much matter an object is made of. Mass is measured in **kilograms, kg**.

Friction

What is friction?

Friction is a force that is exerted when things rub together. Friction can slow things down. The runner's shoes have good grip and make lots of friction with the ground to help her slow down. The duck's feet have very little friction with an icy lake, so it is difficult to stop.

a What kind of surfaces make the most friction?

b What kind of surfaces make the least friction?

Friction can be useful

Friction can be a very useful force. Bikes and cars have brakes that use friction to slow them down or stop them. The surfaces of the brakes rub against the wheels so the wheels don't turn so fast. Some road junctions have a special high-friction surface to slow cars down in case they skid as they stop.

c Give some more examples showing how friction is useful in everyday life.

Reducing friction

Sometimes friction is not useful and we want to reduce it. When two surfaces rub together, they will eventually become worn down because of friction.

Machines have a lot of parts that rub together. To reduce friction, we use substances such as oil and grease. We call these **lubricants**. They make surfaces run smoothly against each other. Surfaces that are smooth or are separated by air have little friction.

Did you know?

A hovercraft rides on a cushion of air. This reduces friction between the hovercraft and the water.

Friction makes things warm

Where there is friction, heat energy is given out. You can feel this happen when you rub your hands together. They feel warm.

Air resistance

Air makes friction with moving objects such as cars and planes. We call this **air resistance**. It slows things down. Parachutists use air resistance to slow them down when they are falling towards the ground. The parachute has a large area, so it makes a lot of air resistance.

Racing cars move very fast. The one in the photo is shaped to keep air resistance low. The parts that move forwards through the air have a small area. We call this a **streamlined** shape. The other car is not as streamlined and will have more air resistance.

If a car has too much air resistance, it will have a high **fuel consumption**. This means that it will use more litres of petrol for each kilometre it travels.

d Sophie's car and Cedric's car both have the same type of engine. Sophie's car does 12 kilometres per litre and Cedric's car does 9 kilometres per litre. Whose car do you think is more streamlined?

Animals that live in water, such as dolphins and sharks, are also streamlined. This reduces the friction between the water and their bodies. Look at the photo opposite. When pelicans dive into water, they put their wings back to make themselves more streamlined.

Questions

1. **a** Describe how the effects of friction can be reduced.
   b Describe how the effects of air resistance can be reduced.

2. Write a story about a world without friction.

3. Draw a design for a car or speedboat that will have very little air resistance.

For your notes

Friction is a force that is exerted when things rub against each other.

Air resistance is a form of friction.

We can reduce or increase friction.

Unbalanced forces

Force arrows

The box in the picture opposite has two forces acting on it. One is the pull of the rope. The other is the weight of the box.

The diagram below shows these forces with **force arrows**. A force arrow points in the direction of the force. The length of the arrow shows the size of the force.

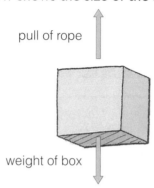

pull of rope

weight of box

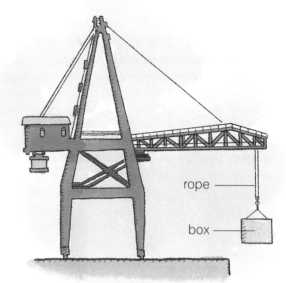

rope

box

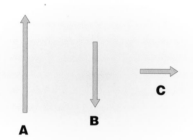

A

B

C

a Which of the arrows **A**, **B** and **C** shows the biggest force?

b Which one shows the smallest force?

c Which one could show someone's weight?

Getting going

If Dipal does not push his go-kart, it will not start moving. A force is needed to start something moving.

Dipal gave his go-kart a gentle push. It did not move at all.

d What force do you think stopped the go-kart moving?

Dipal's push

friction

Dipal gave his go-kart a bigger push. Dipal's push on the go-kart was bigger than friction, so the go-kart started to move.

When forces push against each other like this, and one force is bigger than the other, they are called **unbalanced forces**.

> **When there are unbalanced forces acting on an object, the object starts to move. It moves in the direction of the bigger force and it gets faster.**

Calculating the size of the force

In the diagram opposite, the forces are unbalanced. The big man will push the box towards the small man. We can work out the size of the force that pushed the box:

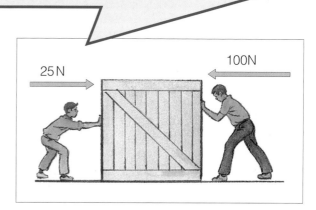

$$100\text{ N} - 25\text{ N} = 75\text{ N}$$

The size of the unbalanced force is sometimes called the **resultant force**. In this example the resultant force is 75 N.

Unbalanced forces on moving objects

Unbalanced forces can act on something that is already moving. The car in the diagram is moving forwards.

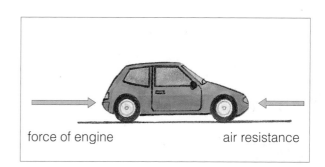

force of engine   air resistance

e The force from the engine is 1000 N and the force from air resistance is 50 N. What is the resultant force?

Because the force from the engine is bigger than the air resistance, the car moves faster.

> **When the bigger force is in the same direction as the movement, the object speeds up. When the bigger force is in the opposite direction to the movement, the object slows down.**

Questions

1. a What happens when there are unbalanced forces acting on an object that is not moving?

   b What happens to a moving object when there are unbalanced forces acting on it and the bigger force is in the same direction as the movement?

   c What happens to a moving object when there are unbalanced forces acting on it and the bigger force is in the opposite direction to the movement?

2. Helen pushed a sledge with force of 8 N. The force of friction pushed against this with a force of 2 N. What is the resultant force?

For your notes

Unbalanced forces can act on an object that is not moving. The object starts to move in the direction of the bigger force.

Unbalanced forces can act on a moving object. If the bigger force is in the same direction as the movement, then the object moves faster. If the bigger force is in the opposite direction to the movement, then the object moves slower.

Staying put

Unbalanced forces make things move. Sometimes forces can act on an object, but the object will stay where it is.

> Why might an object stay where it is even when there are forces acting on it?

Look at the picture of the tug-of-war between Zena and Sam. They are not moving. They are pulling with the same sized force, but in opposite directions. If two forces are the same size and pull in opposite directions, the forces are **balanced**.

a Look at the diagrams below and decide which show balanced forces.

b For each object, say whether it will move or stay still. If it will move, in which direction will it go?

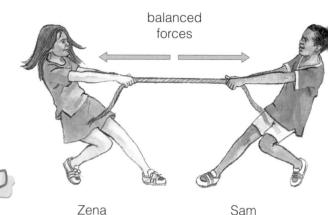

balanced forces

Zena   Sam

A   **B**   **C**   **D**

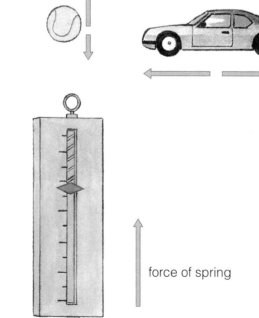

force of spring

weight

Balanced forces

The picture opposite shows a weight hanging from a spring on a newtonmeter. The weight is not moving. The forces on it are balanced. The weight is pulling down on the spring with the same force as the spring pulls up on the weight.

The spring has stretched. The amount it stretches is called the **extension**. There is a relationship between the amount of weight and the extension of the spring.

If the weight is too heavy, the spring will be stretched out of shape. The spring does not return to its original shape when you take the weight off.

116

Mr Blue the decorator stands on a plank of wood to paint a wall. He stands very still. The plank bends because of Mr Blue's weight. It pushes up. This force from the plank is called a **reaction force**. The force pushing down on the plank is the same as the force pushing up on Mr Blue. The forces are balanced.

c What are the forces on your chair when you sit still on it? Draw a diagram with arrows.

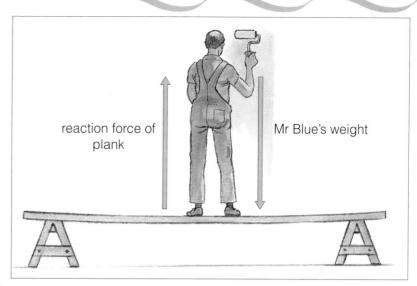

reaction force of plank

Mr Blue's weight

Why do things float and sink?

When an object is put into water, the water pushes up on the object. This force is called **upthrust**. The object pushes down on the water. This force is called **weight**. If the object floats, then the upthrust is equal to the weight. The forces are balanced. If the object sinks, then the upthrust and weight are not equal. The forces are unbalanced.

d Draw a force diagram to show the forces on a floating boat.

Steady speed

When you are travelling in a car at a steady speed, the forward forces are the same as the forces of friction acting against the car. The picture on the right shows this. The forces are balanced when the car is moving at a steady speed. So balanced forces don't only exist when an object is still. They can also exist when an object is moving at a steady speed.

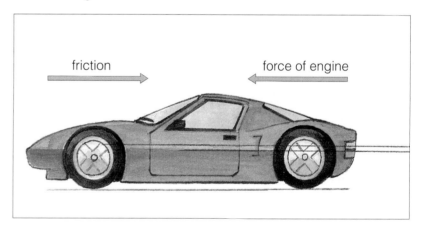

friction

force of engine

Questions

1. Copy the sentences below and say whether the forces are balanced or unbalanced for each one.

   a a car travelling at a steady speed on a motorway

   b a car speeding up to overtake a slow lorry

   c a car slowing down to stop at traffic lights

2. Julie and Jill pull with a joint force of 50 N in one direction, and Jack and Paulo pull in the opposite direction. If the forces are balanced, what force do Jack and Paulo exert?

3. Draw a force diagram showing the forces on an aeroplane travelling at a steady speed.

For your notes

If two forces are the same size and pull in opposite directions, they are called **balanced forces**.

The **reaction force** stops something falling through a solid object. The reaction force balances the weight.

When an object floats, the forces of **weight** and **upthrust** are equal.

Forces

8.6

Speed

Learn about

➤ Speed

Talking about speed

People use different sayings to describe how fast or slow things move.

As fast as the speed of light

As swift as a deer

Slower than a snail

Faster than a speeding bullet

We can tell how fast a thing moves by measuring its **speed**.

How do we measure speed?

To find the speed of an object, you need to know the distance the object travels and the time it takes to travel that distance. You take the distance travelled and divide by the time taken. We can show it like this:

$$\text{speed} = \frac{\text{distance travelled}}{\text{time taken}} \quad \begin{array}{l}\text{(in metres, m)}\\\text{(in seconds, s)}\end{array}$$

Units of speed

We measure distance in metres or kilometres and time in seconds or hours. In science, we measure speed in metres per second, m/s. In everyday life, we find it easier to measure speed in kilometres per hour, km/h.

Example 1

A dog ran 30 metres in 2 seconds.

$$\text{dog's speed} = \frac{30 \text{ metres travelled}}{2 \text{ seconds taken}}$$

$$= \frac{30 \text{ m}}{2 \text{ s}} = 15 \text{ m/s}$$

The dog ran at a speed of 15 metres per second or 15 m/s. This means it ran 15 metres every second.

Example 2

In a sponsored walk at school, Danny walked 8 kilometres in 2 hours.

$$\text{Danny's speed} = \frac{8 \text{ kilometres travelled}}{2 \text{ hours taken}} = \frac{8 \text{ km}}{2 \text{ h}} = 4 \text{ km/h}$$

Danny walked at a speed of 4 kilometres per hour or 4 km/h. This means he walked 4 kilometres every hour.

Calculating speed

a Find the speed of these people.

   i Danny walked 20 kilometres in 4 hours.

   ii Susan ran 100 metres in 20 seconds.

   iii Yin travelled 200 kilometres in 2 hours on a train.

   iv Danny travelled 1600 kilometres in 4 hours in an aeroplane.

   v Yin ran 4800 metres in 20 minutes (give your answer in units of m/s).

How fast do things move?

The picture opposite shows the speeds of some moving objects.

b How far would a snail travel in an hour?

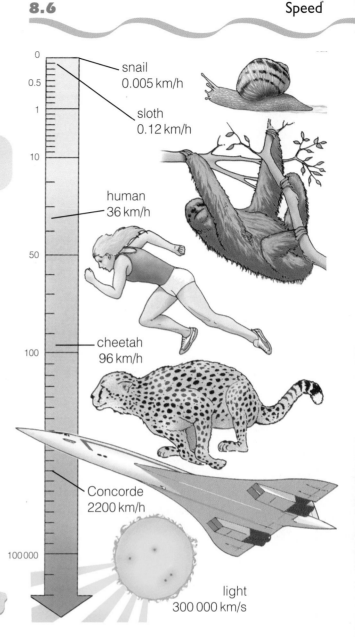

Questions

1. Copy the table below and complete **A** to **E**.

Distance travelled	Time taken	Speed
100 km	2 hours	A
40 metres	B	5 m/s
200 km	4 hours	C
200 km	D	20 km/h
50 km	30 minutes	E

2. Think up some new sayings such as 'faster than a speeding bullet' for the following words:

   a speed   **b** fast   **c** slow.

3. a How far would a cheetah run in half an hour?

   b How long would it take a sloth to travel 0.48 km?

For your notes

Speed is the distance an object travels in a certain time.

$$\text{speed} = \frac{\text{distance travelled (in metres)}}{\text{time taken (in seconds)}}$$

The units used for speed are metres per second, m/s, or kilometres per hour, km/h.

Variables

We link things together using **relationships**. In experiments we find the relationship between variables. A **variable** is the thing that we change or that is changed in an experiment.

In a javelin competition, the more force an athlete uses to throw the javelin, the further it will go. The variables are the force the athlete uses and the distance the javelin travels.

The relationship is:

● the more force the athlete uses, the greater the distance the javelin will travel.

We can also give the relationship as:

● the less force the athlete uses, the smaller the distance the javelin will travel.

Think about

► Relationships

Fast cars

Mary wondered what would happen to the speed of the toy car if she changed the slope.

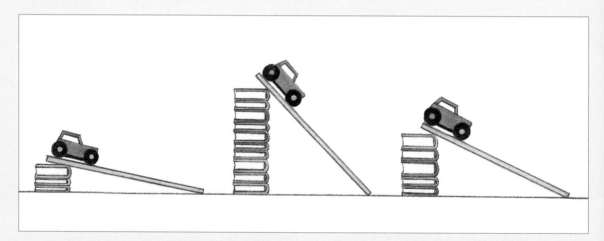

Discuss what you think would happen to the speed of Mary's car.

a What do you think will happen if she makes the slope steeper?

b What do you think will happen if she makes the slope less steep?

c What are the input and outcome variables in this experiment?

d Is there a relationship between the variables? If so, describe it.

Pulling shoes

Kerry carried out an experiment. She attached a newtonmeter to a shoe and pulled it across the floor. She put different weights inside the shoe. Then she measured the extension of the spring on the newtonmeter when the pull was just enough to make the shoe move across the floor.

The table shows the results of the experiment.

e What are the input and outcome variables in the experiment?

f Is there a relationship between the variables? If so, describe it.

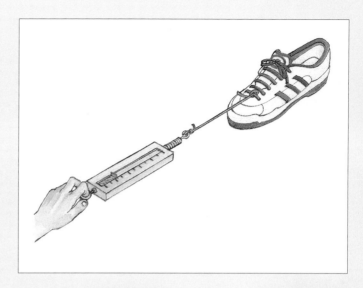

Weight in N	1	2	3	4	5
Extension of spring in mm	10	20	30	40	50

Kerry drew this graph of her results.

g Which variable did she put along the bottom, the input variable or the outcome variable?

h Describe the shape of the graph.

i Predict the extension of the spring if Kerry used a weight of 2.5 N.

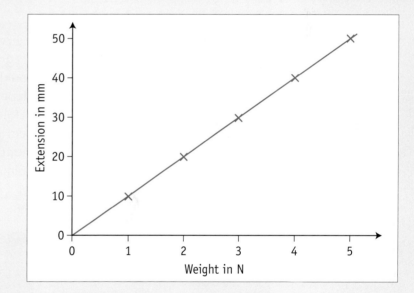

Questions

1. Explain what the following words mean:

   a variable   **b** relationship.

2. The table below shows the force used to push a go-kart and the distance it travelled.

Force in N	10	20	30	40	50
Distance in cm	5	10	15	20	25

   a What are the input and outcome variables in the experiment?

   b Plot a line graph of the results. Put the force along the bottom and the distance up the side. Draw a line of best fit using a ruler.

   c Is there a relationship between the variables? If so, describe it.

A day at the zoo

When will it be born?

Altaf and Rabeya were visiting the zoo one weekend. Mum had also brought along their baby sister Shammin.

Altaf loved watching the elephants. One of the elephants was expecting a baby. Altaf really liked baby elephants. He wondered how long it would be before it was born.

He remembered that Dana his hamster was pregnant for three weeks. He asked his mum if they could come back next month and see the baby elephant. Mum said that it would be quite a while before it was born. Elephants are pregnant for nearly two years! Mum was only pregnant for nine months with Shammin. The length of time that an animal is pregnant is called its **gestation period**.

a How long is the gestation period of a human?

First steps

They went to see the zebras. Rabeya was surprised to see a very small zebra trotting around with one of the other zebras. Mum said that the baby zebra had been born a few weeks ago. Even though it was so young, the baby was already running around. Her sister Shammin was six months old and still could not walk. Mum told her that lots of animals can walk very soon after they are born.

b Human babies don't walk until they are about a year and a half old. Why do they not need to walk sooner than this?

Living in a pouch

They went to see the kangaroos. Altaf could see a baby kangaroo poking its head out of its mother's pouch. The zoo keeper told him that kangaroos are a special kind of mammal called a **marsupial**. These animals have a very short gestation period. They give birth after about five weeks, but the baby is still much too helpless to survive on its own. It crawls into a special pouch and stays in there for another six months. The koala and the wallaby also do this.

c List three things that the pouch provides for the baby kangaroo.

A baby kangaroo just after it is born.

Will it breed?

Everyone was very excited about the new panda that had been flown in from a zoo in Germany. Giant pandas are getting very rare in the wild. Zoos all over the world are trying to stop them dying out. The zoo hoped that the new panda would breed with one of their female pandas and produce a baby panda.

Questions

1. Use the information in the story to put the animals below in order of gestation period, starting with the longest.

   > human   hamster   elephant   kangaroo

2. Why do you think that zebras have to be able to walk very soon after being born, but a newborn lion will be helpless for a few weeks?

3. Draw a flow chart to show the life cycle of a human.

4. What do you think about zoos? Write a letter to the nature magazine *Wild Zone*, either explaining why zoos are good for animals or why you think zoos are bad.

Spot the difference

Making sperm and eggs

The bodies of men and women have some very important differences. Men produce sex cells called **sperm**, and women produce sex cells called **eggs**. To make a baby, a sperm and an egg must join together.

The reproductive systems of a man and a woman are different because they have different functions.

Male reproductive system

The picture opposite shows the male reproductive system. It is shown from the side.

Sperm are made in the **testes**. There are two of these (one on its own is called a **testis**). The testes produce millions of sperm every day. The photo below shows sperm seen under a microscope.

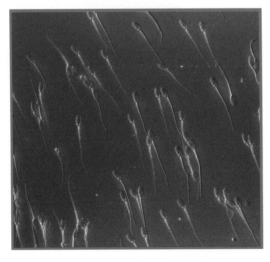

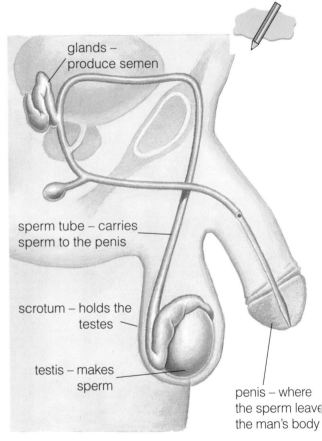

glands – produce semen

sperm tube – carries sperm to the penis

scrotum – holds the testes

testis – makes sperm

penis – where the sperm leave the man's body

The testes are in a special bag of skin called the **scrotum**. This keeps the sperm at just the right temperature. When it is cold, the scrotum gets tighter to keep the testes close to the body to keep them warm. When it is warm, the scrotum gets looser to move the testes away from the body to keep cool.

When the sperm leave the testes, they pass along a tube called the **sperm tube**. This carries the sperm to the penis. On the way the sperm pass two **glands**. These glands add a liquid to the sperm. The sperm and liquid together are called **semen**.

Eventually the sperm pass down the **penis**. This is where they leave the man's body.

Female reproductive system

The picture opposite shows the female reproductive system. It is shown from the front. The photo below shows an egg seen under a microscope.

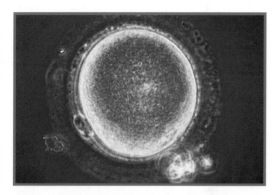

The eggs are made in the **ovaries**. There are two ovaries, one on each side. Once a month an egg leaves one of the ovaries and passes down the **oviduct** (egg tube). This takes a few days. The egg and sperm may meet in the oviduct.

The **uterus** (womb) is where the baby will develop. The opening of the uterus is called the **cervix**. This is a ring of muscle that can open quite wide to let the baby out when it is ready to be born.

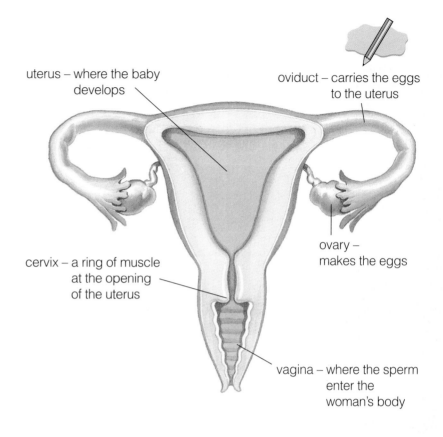

uterus – where the baby develops

oviduct – carries the eggs to the uterus

ovary – makes the eggs

cervix – a ring of muscle at the opening of the uterus

vagina – where the sperm enter the woman's body

Questions

1. Copy and complete these sentences.

   a Sperm are made in the _____. When the sperm leave the testes, they pass down the _____. Glands add a special liquid to make _____. The sperm then leave through the _____.

   b Eggs are made in the _____. Every month an egg is released and passes down the _____ to the _____.

2. What happens in the uterus?

3. Why is the cervix made of muscle?

4. a Some men who do not want to have any more children will have a vasectomy. This is an operation in which the sperm tubes are closed up. Explain how this will stop them making babies.

   b A woman may have a similar operation. The oviducts are closed up. Explain how this will stop her having children.

For your notes

Sperm are made in the **testes**. They pass down the **sperm tube** and out of the **penis**.

Eggs are made in the **ovaries**. They pass down the **oviduct** to the **uterus**.

A new generation

How the sperm and egg meet

To make a baby, the male and female sex cells must meet and join together. When a man and a woman make love, the man's penis enters the woman's vagina. Sperm are released from the penis into the vagina. This is how the sperm get into the body of the woman. It is called **sexual intercourse**. The sperm then swim towards the egg.

Did you know?

Up to 500 million sperm are released into the vagina.

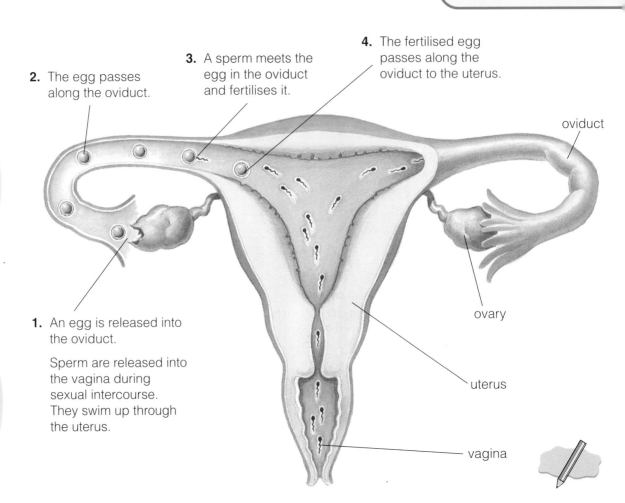

2. The egg passes along the oviduct.

3. A sperm meets the egg in the oviduct and fertilises it.

4. The fertilised egg passes along the oviduct to the uterus.

oviduct

1. An egg is released into the oviduct.

Sperm are released into the vagina during sexual intercourse. They swim up through the uterus.

ovary

uterus

vagina

What happens to the sperm?

What happens next depends on whether an egg has been released into the oviduct.

● The sperm start to swim up from the vagina into the uterus. Many sperm die on the way.

● The sperm swim up through the uterus and then into both oviducts.

If there is no egg in the oviducts:

● All the sperm will die in a short time.

● No baby will be produced.

If there is an egg in the oviduct:

- The sperm will surround it, as shown in photo **A**.

- The first sperm to reach the egg burrows into it. Photo **B** shows this.

- The nucleus of the sperm joins with the nucleus of the egg. This is called **fertilisation**.

- The fertilised egg will become a baby. The woman is pregnant.

 a What happens to the sperm if there is no egg in the oviducts?

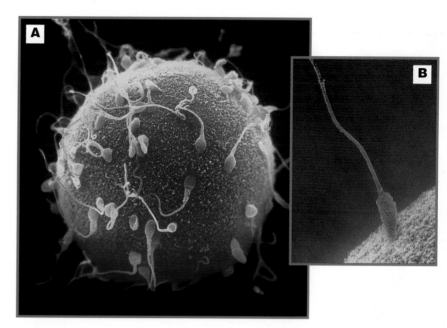

Twins

Sometimes a woman gives birth to more than one baby at the same time. Two babies together are called **twins**. Twins can be produced in two ways.

Identical twins, like Hannah and Mary, are produced from just one egg. The egg splits into two just after it starts to develop into a baby. Because both Hannah and Mary came from the same egg and sperm, they look exactly the same.

Non-identical twins, like Charlie and Amy, are produced if two eggs are released at the same time. Each egg is then fertilised by a different sperm. These twins are no more alike or different than any other brothers and sisters.

Lots of babies

Some women are not able to have a baby naturally. They can be given drugs which make them release lots of eggs in one go. Then there is more chance of a sperm meeting one of the eggs. Sometimes more than one egg is fertilised and the woman can be pregnant with five, six or even seven babies!

b Do you think that these babies will look identical? Explain your answer.

Questions

1. Why do you think so many sperm are produced?

2. Explain what fertilisation means.

3. Imagine that you are a sperm. Write a story about your journey to the egg. Include all the parts of the body that you swim through.

4. Explain the difference in the way identical twins and non-identical twins are produced.

For your notes

In **sexual intercourse**, millions of sperm are released into the woman's vagina. Most will die, but one may make it to the egg.

Fertilisation happens when the nucleus of a sperm joins up with the nucleus of an egg.

Pregnancy

From egg to baby

After an egg is fertilised, it settles in the thick, soft lining of the uterus. This is called **implantation**. It grows into a tiny ball of cells called the **embryo**. When this happens the woman is **pregnant**. The embryo then grows more to become a **fetus**.

a What happens to the egg after fertilisation?

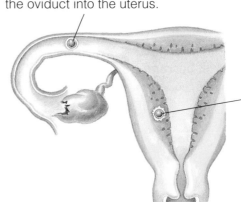

The fertilised egg passes along the oviduct into the uterus.

Implantation – it settles in the spongy lining of the uterus.

The growing baby

The photos show the development of the fetus during pregnancy.

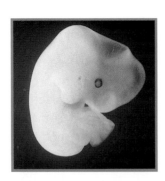

At about 4 weeks the embryo's heart starts to beat. It has eyes, ears and legs.

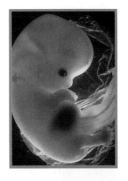

By about 9 weeks, the baby is called a fetus. It has a head, arms and legs. Fingers and toes start to develop.

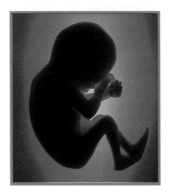

At around 22 weeks, the doctor can hear the baby's heartbeat. Its lungs are starting to develop. Its mother will feel it kicking.

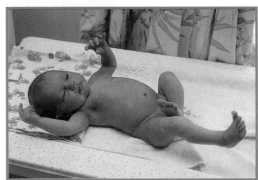

At 39 weeks, when it is born, the baby is fully developed. It has a lot of fat to keep it warm when it is born.

b What differences can you see between the pictures at 4 weeks and 39 weeks?

c Sometimes babies are born before 39 weeks, perhaps as early as 26 weeks. What special care do you think these babies need?

Getting what it needs

The embryo gets all the substances it needs from the mother's body, through the **placenta**. This forms in the uterus early in pregnancy. The **cord** links the embryo to the placenta.

The blood in the cord carries food and oxygen to the embryo from the placenta, and it carries carbon dioxide and other waste substances back. The mother usually eats more food when she is pregnant because she is feeding the baby inside her. The diagram below shows the fetus just before birth. The fetus usually lies upside down with its arms tucked close to its body. This is the best position for an easy birth.

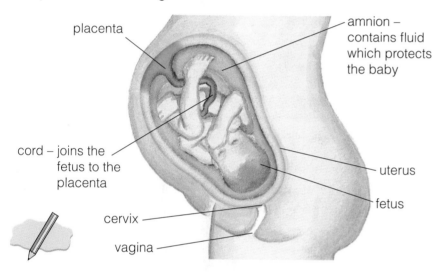

placenta

amnion – contains fluid which protects the baby

cord – joins the fetus to the placenta

uterus

fetus

cervix

vagina

d What is the job of the placenta?

The mother's body has to adapt ready for when the baby is born. Her breasts grow, preparing for breast feeding after birth.

Birth

Pregnancy lasts for about nine months. Then the baby is born. It is pushed out of the uterus by **contractions**. These happen when the strong muscles of the uterus wall squeeze.

The diagram on the left shows a baby at 39 weeks ready to be born. Its head is positioned downwards to come out first. If the baby's head does not come out first during birth, there can be problems. The mother may need more help from the doctor.

The baby is still attached to the mother by the cord. The cord has to be cut and tied. The placenta is no longer needed and leaves the uterus a few minutes later. This is called the **afterbirth**.

Now the mother produces milk as food for the baby. All mammals make food for their young in the mammary glands. This milk is very nutritious. The baby gets its oxygen from breathing air.

e Why is the afterbirth no longer needed?

Questions

1. Write out each part along with its correct job.

Parts	Jobs
amnion	joins the placenta to the fetus
cord	supplies the fetus with food and oxygen
placenta	pushed out of the uterus after the baby is born
afterbirth	protects the baby from bumps

2. Describe the ways the mother's body changes during pregnancy.

3. Describe what happens when the baby is born.

4. Produce a leaflet explaining to parents how the baby develops inside the mother and how it is born after nine months.

For your notes

It takes nine months for a human baby to develop fully inside its mother. This is called **pregnancy**.

Adolescence

Learn about

► Adolescence

► Menstrual cycle

All change!

Adolescence is a time in everyone's life when physical and emotional changes happen. The changes prepare us to be young adults. The changes happen at different times in different people.

Puberty is the first part of adolescence. Most of the physical changes take place during puberty. Puberty usually starts earlier in girls than it does in boys. In puberty, young people often find that their emotions and behaviour change. They become more attracted to the opposite sex.

Adolescence finishes when people stop growing, at about the age of 18 years.

(a) What happens in adolescence?

During puberty

Many changes happen to boys and girls in puberty. These changes are brought about by substances called **hormones**. The testes in boys make the hormone **testosterone**. The ovaries in girls make the hormone **oestrogen**.

(b) What are hormones?

The changes that happen at puberty are listed in the table. Some are also shown in the picture below.

Changes in boys	Changes in girls
Sudden increase in height (growth spurt)	Sudden increase in height (growth spurt)
Hair starts to grow on body, including pubic hair	Hair starts to grow on body, including pubic hair
Voice deepens	Breasts grow
Testes start to make sperm and hormones	Ovaries start to release eggs and make hormones
Shoulders broaden	Hips widen
Sexual organs get bigger	Periods start

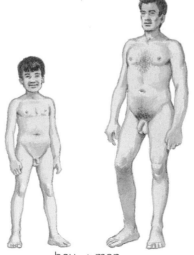

boy → man

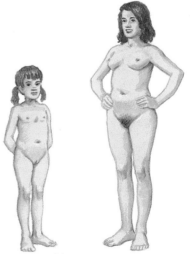

girl → woman

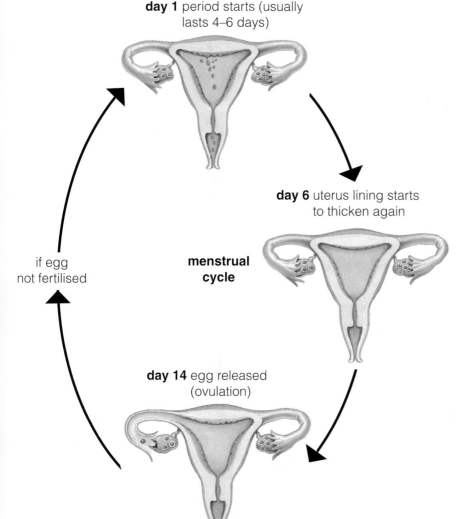

day 1 period starts (usually lasts 4–6 days)

day 6 uterus lining starts to thicken again

menstrual cycle

if egg not fertilised

day 14 egg released (ovulation)

The menstrual cycle

During puberty, girls start a monthly cycle called the **menstrual cycle**. The cycle lasts about 28 days and is controlled by hormones. The hormones cause an egg to develop and be released in each cycle. The lining of the uterus builds up and becomes soft and spongy.

If the egg is fertilised, it becomes implanted in this lining. If the egg is not fertilised, the soft lining is not needed for the embryo. The lining made of dead cells and blood breaks down and leaves the body through the vagina. This is known as a **period**. We say that the period starts on day 1 of the cycle, as the diagram opposite shows.

c What is a period?

Women usually stop having periods between the ages of 45 and 55 years. This is called **menopause**. They also stop having periods while they are pregnant.

d When do women stop having periods?

Questions

1. Write out each word along with its explanation.

   Words

   period   puberty   adolescence   hormones   menopause

   Explanations

   - a time in everyone's life when physical and emotional changes take place
   - the first part of adolescence in which most of these changes take place
   - substances that cause the changes in boys and girls
   - dead cells and blood leave the body through the vagina
   - time when women stop having periods

2. **a** Describe three changes that happen to boys during puberty.

   b Describe three changes that happen to girls during puberty.

3. What are the hormones called that cause the changes in puberty in boys and girls?

4. Explain what happens in the menstrual cycle:

   a between day 1 and day 4

   b at about day 14

   c at about day 6.

For your notes

Adolescence is a time when physical and emotional changes happen.

Puberty is the first part of adolescence when most of the physical changes happen.

Pregnant pause

Time to develop

An elephant is pregnant for a lot longer than a hamster. You are going to investigate some reasons for this. Here is some data showing the length of time that different animals are pregnant. The animals are in order of size.

a Plot a bar chart showing the gestation period for each animal.

Now look carefully at the pattern of the results.

b Describe the relationship between animal size and gestation period.

c Explain why you think this happens, using as much science as you can.

d Are there any results that look out of place?

e What do you already know about this animal that may explain why it doesn't fit the pattern?

f Can you predict the gestation period of a rabbit?

Animal	Gestation period in days
Mouse	21
Squirrel	30
Cat	62
Kangaroo	40
Ape	200
Human	280
Camel	355
Rhino	420
Elephant	649

Did you know?

Rabbits have a shorter gestation period than humans. They can also have more babies at once. Rabbits have a double uterus, and each side can have several baby rabbits developing in it at the same time.

Predators and prey

One way of putting animals in order of size is to measure their mass. Here is some data for three more animals. They are all predators.

Animal	Average adult mass in kg	Gestation period in days
Cheetah	95	60
Lion	190	108
Tiger	210	109

g Draw a line graph of gestation period against adult mass. Use blue to plot the points and join them with a curved line. Label this line 'predators'.

This table shows data for three prey animals.

Animal	Average adult mass in kg	Gestation period in days
Antelope	45	180
Wildebeest	200	255
Zebra	280	360

h Add this data to your graph. Use red to plot these points and join them with a curved line. Label this line 'prey'.

i Do your graphs show a pattern? If so, describe it.

j Which animals tend to have the longer gestation period compared with their body mass, predators or prey?

When lions and tigers are born, they are blind and helpless for a week or so. They cannot move very far, so the mother has to stay in one place to look after them, or carry them around. A baby zebra is very different. It can walk with the rest of the herd only a few hours after it is born.

k Prey animals are at risk from predators. Prey animals are pregnant longer than predators. Suggest two ways this helps the prey animals.

adaptation Having features that help a living thing to survive in a particular place.

adapted A well adapted organism has features that help it to survive in a particular place.

adolescence The time in a young person's life when physical and emotional changes happen.

afterbirth The placenta comes out of the uterus after the baby is born. It is called the afterbirth.

air resistance The friction a moving object makes with air.

ammeter An instrument to measure current.

amphibians One of the groups of vertebrate animals. Amphibians lay eggs in water but breathe air. They have a smooth moist skin.

amplitude The distance between the top of a vibration and the middle of the vibration.

amps Current is measured in amps. The short way of writing amps is A.

animal cells The building blocks that make up all animals. Animal cells have a cell membrane, cytoplasm and a nucleus.

anther The part of the stamen in a flower that makes the pollen.

arthropods Group of invertebrate animals with segmented bodies and jointed legs.

atom The smallest part of an element.

attract To pull together.

bacteria A group of microorganisms. Some bacteria cause disease.

balanced equation A chemical equation is balanced because there is the same amount of material on both sides.

balanced forces Two forces of the same size pulling in opposite directions.

birds One of the groups of vertebrate animals. Birds lay eggs with a hard shell, look after their young and have feathers and wings.

blubber A thick layer of fat that some animals have to help them keep warm.

boiling point The temperature at which a substance changes from a liquid to a gas.

camouflage Features that help a living thing to blend in with its surroundings.

carbon dioxide A compound made when carbon burns and joins with oxygen.

carbon An element that is in coal and other fuels.

carpel The female parts of a flower, that produce the egg cells.

cathode ray oscilloscope A machine that shows vibrations as a squiggle on a screen. Cathode ray oscilloscope may be written as CRO for short.

cell membrane A thin layer that surrounds the cell and controls the movement of substances in and out of the cell.

cell wall A tough box around plant cells.

cells Tiny building blocks that make up all living things.

cellulose A tough stringy substance found in plant cell walls.

centipedes One of the groups of arthropods. Centipedes have lots of legs and a segmented body.

cervix A ring of muscle at the opening of the uterus.

change of state Changing from a solid to a liquid or a liquid to a gas and back again.

chemical change A change that makes a new substance. Many chemical changes are irreversible.

chemical energy Energy stored in a material, which will be given out in a chemical reaction.

chemical reaction A change that makes a new substance.

chloride A compound that contains chlorine atoms.

chlorophyll A green substance that is needed for photosynthesis.

chloroplasts The parts of a plant cell that carry out photosynthesis.

chromatogram The result of a chromatography experiment, that shows how far each substance travelled up the paper.

chromatography A method used to separate mixtures of substances. The most soluble substances travel the furthest up the paper.

circuit Batteries and lamps joined up by wires to make a closed loop.

classification Putting things with similar features into the same group.

combustion The chemical reaction that happens when something burns.

complete circuit Batteries and lamps joined up by wires to make a closed loop.

compound microscope A microscope that uses more than one lens to magnify things.

compound A substance that contains more than one type of atom joined together.

condensing Changing from a gas to a liquid.

conduct To pass along. Thermal energy can be conducted. Electrical energy can be conducted.

conductor A material that passes along thermal energy is a good conductor of thermal energy. A material that passes along electrical energy is a good conductor of electricity.

conservation of energy The idea that energy is passed from place to place but is hard to create or destroy.

continuous variation Differences in features that can have a range of values, such as height.

contractions The muscles of the uterus wall squeeze when a baby is born.

copper oxide The compound that is made when copper burns and joins with oxygen in the air.

cord This links the developing baby to the placenta in a pregnant female animal.

core A magnetic material put inside a coil to make an electromagnet.

corrosion The process by which metals change over time. Rusting is one sort of corrosion.

crustaceans One of the groups of arthropods. Crustaceans have lots of legs, a soft body and usually a hard shell.

current How fast the electricity goes around the circuit.

cytoplasm A jelly-like substance found inside cells.

decibel Loudness of sound is measured in decibels. The short way of writing decibels is dB.

dense A dense material has a lot of particles in a small volume.

density How heavy a material is for its size.

discontinuous variation Differences in features that can be one thing or the other, such as curly or straight hair.

dissolve The particles of a solid break apart and mix with the particles of a liquid.

distillation A method used to separate mixtures of liquids with different boiling points.

distilled water Water that has been made pure. It has been changed to a gas and condensed back to a liquid again.

eardrum A small 'drumskin' inside the ear which vibrates when sounds reach it.

egg cell The female sex cell in a plant. An egg cell joins with a pollen grain to make an embryo plant.

egg The female sex cell in an animal. An egg joins with a sperm to make a baby.

electrical energy Energy carried by electricity.

electromagnet A coil of wire with an iron core and a current through the wire.

electron microscope A microscope that uses electrons instead of light. It makes things look very much larger.

element A substance that contains only one type of atom.

embryo A tiny ball of cells formed from the fertilised egg in animal reproduction.

embryo plant A new plant inside a seed ready to grow.

energy conservation The idea that energy is passed from place to place but is hard to create or destroy.

energy transfer The movement of energy from one place to another.

energy When anything happens, energy is transferred. Energy makes things work.

evaporating Changing from a liquid to a gas.

extension The amount a spring stretches when you hang a weight on it.

features Special parts of organisms, or particular things they do.

fertilisation In an animal, a sperm joining with an egg to make a baby. In a plant, a pollen grain joining with an egg cell to make an embryo plant.

fetus A developing baby inside the uterus of a female mammal.

filament Part of the stamen in a flower. The filament supports the anther.

filament lamp An electric light with a piece of wire that forms part of the circuit. The wire (the filament) glows when electricity passes through it.

fish One of the groups of vertebrate animals. Fish live in water and lay eggs there. They breathe through gills and have scales and fins.

flammable A flammable material burns easily.

flatworms One of the groups of invertebrate animals. Flatworms have a flat leaf-shaped body.

force arrows Arrows we draw that point in the direction of a force. The length shows the size of the force.

freezing Changing from a liquid to a solid.

frequency The number of vibrations that happen in a second.

friction The force that is made when things rub together.

fruit A structure made in a flower, that contains the seed. It is formed from the ovary.

fuel A material that has a lot of stored chemical energy. We burn a fuel to use the energy.

fuel consumption The amount of fuel a vehicle uses to travel a certain distance. Fuel consumption is measured in kilometres per litre or miles per gallon.

gas A state of matter that is not very dense. A gas is easily squashed. Its shape and volume can change.

gestation period The time a baby takes to develop inside its mother before it is born.

glands Parts that make hormones and other substances in animals. In male animals, the glands in the reproductive system make a liquid which mixes with sperm to make semen.

gravitational energy Energy stored because something is lifted up.

gravitational force The force exerted by one object on another object.

gravity The force that pulls everything towards the centre of the Earth. The other planets, the Moon and the Sun also pull things because of gravity.

greenhouse effect The carbon dioxide in the air stops some of the heat energy escaping from the Earth. It behaves like the glass in a greenhouse. The greenhouse effect may increase, making the Earth warmer.

group A vertical column in the periodic table.

habitat The place where an animal lives.

heat energy Energy transferred from a hot object to a cooler object.

hertz Frequency is measured in hertz. The short way of writing hertz is Hz.

hormone A substance in the body that makes changes happen.

hydrocarbon A substance that contains only carbon and hydrogen atoms.

identical twins Two babies that came from the same sperm and egg. They are born at the same time and they look exactly the same.

implantation In animal reproduction, a fertilised egg settles into the soft lining of the uterus.

inherited features Features that are passed on from the parents.

input variable The thing you change in an investigation.

insects One of the groups of arthropods. Insects have six legs and three parts to the body.

insoluble A substance that is insoluble will not dissolve.

insulate To prevent thermal energy or electrical energy passing through.

invertebrate An animal without a backbone.

iron oxide The compound that is made when iron burns and joins with oxygen in the air.

irreversible change A change that cannot be changed back to how it was before.

jellyfish One of the groups of invertebrate animals. Jellyfish have a soft jelly-like body.

joules Energy is measured in joules. The short way of writing joules is J.

kilogram Mass is measured in kilograms. The short way of writing kilograms is kg.

kilohertz There are 1000 hertz in 1 kilohertz. The short way of writing kilohertz is kHz.

kilojoules There are 1000 joules in 1 kilojoule. The short way of writing kilojoules is kJ.

kinetic energy The scientific name for movement energy.

light energy Energy transferred by light.

light microscope Another name for a compound microscope.

limewater A solution used to test for carbon dioxide. Limewater turns milky when carbon dioxide bubbles through it.

liquid A state of matter that flows. The shape of a liquid can change, but its volume is fixed.

loudness The volume of a sound. The more energy the sound has, the louder it is.

lubricant A substance that reduces friction by making surfaces run smoothly against each other.

magnesium oxide The compound that is made when magnesium burns and joins with oxygen in the air.

magnet An object that makes a magnetic field.

magnetic field A space where magnetic materials are pulled.

magnetic field line The lines that iron filings make when they are in a magnetic field.

magnetic material A material that is attracted by a magnet.

magnification Making something look bigger.

mammals One of the groups of vertebrate animals. Mammals have hairy skin. Their babies develop inside the mother and are fed on milk.

mammary glands Features that female mammals have, that make milk.

marsupial A type of mammal. The baby develops in its mother's pouch.

mass A measure of how much matter an object has.

material Anything that is made up of particles. A material may be an element, a compound or a mixture.

matter Anything that has mass is made up of matter. Matter contains particles.

melting point The temperature at which a substance changes from a solid to a liquid.

melting Changing from a solid to a liquid.

menopause Time in a woman's life when her periods stop.

menstrual cycle A monthly cycle in women. During the cycle an egg is released, and the woman has a period.

metal A material that is shiny and conducts electrical and thermal energy.

microorganism A very small living thing that can only be seen with a microscope.

microscope A device that is used for looking at very small objects.

microscopic Something that can only be seen with a microscope is microscopic.

millipedes One of the groups of arthropods. Millipedes have lots of legs and a segmented body.

mixture A material that contains more than one substance.

model An idea or picture made up by a scientist to show a situation that cannot be seen. A model helps scientists think through explanations.

molecule A group of two or more atoms joined together.

molluscs One of the groups of invertebrate animals. Molluscs have a soft muscular body with a foot, and usually a hard shell.

moulting Hair or feathers fall off an animal when it moults.

movement energy When something moves, it has movement energy.

newton Force is measured in newtons. The short way of writing newtons is N.

non-identical twins Two babies that came from different sperm and eggs. They are born at the same time, but look different.

non-metal A material that is not a metal.

nucleus The part of a cell that controls everything the cell does.

oestrogen A hormone in female animals that makes changes happen at puberty.

ore A rock that contains a metal. The metal is obtained from the ore by a chemical reaction.

organism A living thing, that carries out the processes of life.

outcome variable The thing that changes during an investigation. The outcome variable is the thing you measure.

ovary In an animal, part of the female reproductive system that makes the eggs. In a plant, part of the carpel that makes the egg cells.

oviduct A tube in the reproductive system of a female animal. The eggs travel down the oviduct to the uterus.

oxide A compound that contains oxygen atoms. An oxide is made when a substance burns and joins with oxygen in the air.

oxygen One of the gases in the air. We need oxygen to stay alive, and burning uses oxygen.

palisade cells The cells in a leaf where photosynthesis takes place.

parallel circuit A circuit with more than one loop.

particle model The idea that everything is made up of particles.

particles Tiny parts that make up every type of matter.

penis Part of the reproductive system in a male animal. The penis allows the sperm to be placed inside the vagina.

period A horizontal row in the periodic table.

period Part of a woman's menstrual cycle. The lining of the uterus breaks down and leaves the body through the vagina.

periodic table The table showing all the elements.

photosynthesis Plants make food by photosynthesis. They turn carbon dioxide and water into sugars and oxygen, using light energy.

physical change A change in which no new substance is made. A change of state is a physical change. Physical changes are reversible.

pitch How high (squeaky) or low (bass) a sound is.

placenta Structure formed in a pregnant female mammal. The developing baby gets its food and oxygen from the placenta.

plant cells The building blocks that make up all plants. Plant cells have a cell membrane, cytoplasm and a nucleus, and also a cell wall, chloroplasts and a vacuole.

pollen grain The male sex cell in a plant. A pollen grain joins with an egg cell to make an embryo plant.

pollination The transfer of pollen from an anther to a stigma in plant reproduction.

pregnant A female animal is pregnant when there is a baby growing inside her uterus.

property How something looks, or how it behaves. The properties of a material include its colour, strength and hardness.

puberty The first part of adolescence, when physical changes happen.

pure A pure material only contains one substance.

range The different values that are possible, such as all the different heights in a group of people.

reaction A change in which a new substance is made.

reaction force A force that stops things falling through solid objects. When you sit on a chair, your weight is balanced by the reaction force from the chair.

relationship A pattern that links variables together. A relationship describes how the outcome variable changes when the input variable is changed.

repel To push apart.

reptiles One of the groups of vertebrate animals. Reptiles breathe air and lay eggs on land. They have a scaly dry skin.

resultant force The size of an unbalanced force, which makes the object move or speed up or slow down.

reversible change A change that can be changed back to how it was before.

root hairs Tiny structures on a root that absorb water from the soil.

roundworms One of the groups of invertebrate animals. Roundworms have a soft thin round body.

rust The substance that is formed when iron corrodes. Rust is iron oxide.

saturated A solution is saturated when no more of a substance can dissolve in it.

scale diagram A drawing that shows something bigger or smaller than it really is.

scale factor A number used in scale drawing. You multiply by the scale factor to scale something up. You divide by the scale factor to scale it down.

scaling down Making something smaller.

scaling up Making something bigger.

scrotum Part of the reproductive system in a male animal. The scrotum is a bag of skin that holds the testes.

seed A structure made in a flower, that contains the new embryo plant and a food store.

segmented worms One of the groups of invertebrate animals. Segmented worms have a soft ringed body.

segments Sections of the body in arthropods and segmented worms.

semen A mixture of sperm and a special liquid to help them swim.

series circuit A circuit in which everything is in one loop.

sexual intercourse The man's penis enters the woman's vagina, and sperm are released into the vagina.

solid A state of matter that is dense and has a fixed shape and volume.

soluble A substance that is soluble will dissolve.

solute The substance that dissolves to make a solution.

solution A mixture of a solute dissolved in a solvent.

solvent A liquid that substances can dissolve in.

sound energy Energy transferred by sound.

species A particular type of animal or plant. Members of a species can reproduce to form more of their kind.

speed How fast something is moving.

sperm tube A tube in the reproductive system of a male animal. Sperm swim from the testis to the penis through the sperm tube.

sperm The male sex cell in an animal. The sperm swims to the egg and joins with it to make a baby.

spiders One of the groups of arthropods. Spiders have eight legs and two parts to the body.

stain A material that makes cells show up well under a microscope.

stainless steel A type of steel that does not rust.

stamens The male parts of a flower, that produce the pollen.

starfish One of the groups of invertebrate animals. Starfish have a hard star-shaped body.

states of matter The three states of matter are solids, liquids and gases.

stigma Part of the carpel in a flower. The pollen lands on the stigma.

stomata Holes in a leaf's surface. Gases get in and out of the leaf through the stomata.

strain energy Energy stored in a material because the material is being pulled or pushed.

streamlined A way of shaping things such as cars to keep air resistance low.

style Part of the carpel in a flower. The pollen tube grows down through the style.

substance A material that is always made up from the same atoms arranged in the same way. A substance may be an element or a compound.

sulphide A compound that contains sulphur atoms.

surroundings Everything around a living thing, including its diet and the way it lives.

symbol The letter or letters used to stand for an element.

testes Parts of the reproductive system in a male animal. The testes make the sperm. One on its own is called a testis.

testosterone A hormone in male animals that makes changes happen at puberty.

thermal energy The scientific name for heat energy.

transferring energy Moving energy from one place to another.

twins Two babies that develop together inside the mother and are born at the same time.

unbalanced forces Forces pushing in different directions when one force is bigger than the other. An unbalanced force makes the object move or speed up or slow down.

upthrust The force caused by water pushing up against an object.

uterus Part of the reproductive system in a female animal. The baby grows and develops in the uterus.

vacuole A bag inside plant cells that contains a liquid which keeps the cell firm.

vagina Opening to the reproductive system in a female animal. Sperm enter the woman's body through the vagina, and the baby leaves through the vagina when it is born.

value A measurement or observation.

variable A thing that we change or that changes in an investigation.

variation The differences between members of a species.

veins These transport water, minerals and sugars around a plant.

vertebrate An animal with a backbone.

vibrating Moving up and down or side to side.

vibration A movement up and down or side to side.

virus A group of microorganisms that cause disease.

voltage You get a voltage where energy enters or leaves a circuit.

voltmeter An instrument used to measure voltage.

volts Voltage is measured in volts. The short way of writing volts is V.

water vapour Water that has turned to a gas.

weight The force of gravity on an object, that makes it feel heavy.

word equation An equation in words to show a chemical reaction.

Note: page numbers in **bold** show where a word is **explained** in the text. Words are also explained in the Glossary on pages 134–43.

The authors and publishers would like to thank the following for permission to use photographs:

Cover photos: Tower arch, Tony Stone Images. **Blue spotted coral trout,** Oxford Scientific Films/Mark Webster. **Radio telescope at night,** Science Photo Library/David Nunuk.

1.1a, Gareth Boden. **1.1b**, Empics. **1.1c**, Empics. **1.1d**, J. Allan Cash Ltd. **1.1e**, Robert Harding Picture Library. **1.1f**, J. Allan Cash Ltd. **1.1g**, Trevor Hill. **1.1h**, Tony Stone Images. **1.2**, Robert Harding. **1.3**, Mary Evans Picture Library. **1.4a x 3**, Alan Edwards. **1.4b**, AKG Photo Library. **1.6a**, J. Allan Cash Ltd. **1.6b**, Gareth Boden. **1.6c**, Kobal Collection. **1.7**, Holt Studios. **2.2a**, Trevor Hill. **2.2b**, Holt Studios. **2.2c**, Gareth Boden. **2.2d**, Tony Stone Images. **2.2d**, Science Photo Library/Richard Folwell. **2.5a-b**, Gareth Boden. **2.6**, J. Allan Cash Ltd. **3.2a**, Still Pictures/Ron Gilling. **3.2b**, Still Pictures/Francois Gilson. **3.2c**, Oxford Scientific Films/Harry Taylor. **3.2d**, Hans Reinhard. **3.2e**, Oxford Scientific Films/John Downer. **3.2f**, Oxford Scientific Films/Scott Camazine/CDC. **3.2g**, Science Photo Library/Dr. Linda Stannard. **3.2h**, Oxford Scientific Films/David M. Dennis. **3.2i**, Bruce Coleman. **3.2j**, Mary Evans Picture Library. **3.3a-b**, PhotoDisc. **3.3c**, Oxford Scientific Films/Maurice Tibbles. **3.3d**, PhotoDisc. **3.3e**, Bruce Coleman. **3.3f**, FLPA/ Images of Nature/John Hawkins. **3.3g**, Oxford Scientific Films/Souricat. **3.3h**, Bruce Coleman. **3.3i**, Oxford Scientific Films/Max Gibbs. **3.4a**, Oxford Scientific Films/Fredrik Ehren Strom. **3.4b**, Bruce Coleman. **3.4c**, Oxford Scientific Films/Rudie Kuiter. **3.4d**, Oxford Scientific Films/London Scientific Film. **3.4e**, Oxford Scientific Films/David Fox. **3.4f**, FLPA/Images of Nature/Gerard Laci. **3.4g**, Oxford Scientific Films/Frank Schneidermever. **3.4h**, Bruce Coleman. **3.4i**, Bruce Coleman/Animal Ark. **3.4j**, Oxford Scientific Films/Mills Tandy. **3.5a**, NHPA/Darek Karp. **3.5b**, Oxford Scientific Films/Johnny Johnson. **3.5c**, Tony Stone Images. **3.6a**, Still Pictures/Fred Bruennar. **3.6b**, Oxford Scientific Films/Norbert Rosing. **3.6c**, Oxford Scientific Films/Colin Monteath. **3.6d**, Oxford Scientific Films/Mike Brown. **3.6e**, Oxford Scientific Films/Leszczynski. **4.1a-b**, J. Allan Cash Ltd. **4.1c**, Tony Stone Images. **4.2a**, Robert Harding Picture Library/Shout/P. Allen. **4.3a**, Peter Gould. **4.3a**, Robert Harding Picture Library. **4.3b**, Gareth Boden. **4.3c**, Peter Gould. **4.3d**, Gareth Boden. **4.4a**, Gareth Boden. **4.4b**, Tony Stone Images. **4.5a x 2**, Tony Stone Images. **4.5b**, Peter Gould. **4.7**, Robert Harding Picture Library. **5.1a**, Science Photo Library/Tek Image. **5.1b**, Mary Evans Picture Library. **5.1c**, Image Select/Ann Ronan. **5.1d**, Mary Evans Picture Library. **5.7a-b**, Gareth Boden. **5.7c-h**, Peter Gould. **5.8a**, Gareth Boden. **5.8b**, Robert Harding Picture Library/Shout/Hall. **6.1a**, Science Photo Library/Volker Steger, Peter Arnold Inc. **6.1b**, Gareth Boden. **6.1c**, Biophoto Associates. **6.2a**, Trevor Hill. **6.2b-c**, Biophoto Associates. **6.2d**, Science Photo Library/M.I. Walker. **6.3a**, Bruce Coleman. **6.4a**, Science Photo Library/Adam Hart Davis. **6.4b**, Biophoto Associates. **6.5a**, Holt Studios/Nigel Cattlin. **6.5b**, Biophoto Associates. **6.6a**, Holt Studios/Nigel Cattlin. **6.6b**, Science Photo Library/Andrew Syred. **7.1a-c, e**, Ancient Art & Architecture Collection. **7.1d**, J. Allan Cash Ltd. **7.1f**, Robert Harding Picture Library. **7.2a**, Gareth Boden. **7.2b**, Peter Gould. **7.2c-d**, Gareth Boden. **7.4a x 7**, Peter Gould. **7.4b**, Gareth Boden. **7.4c**, Robert Harding Picture Library. **7.4d**, Gareth Boden. **7.4e**, Robert Harding Picture Library. **7.6a**, Science Photo Library/Jerry Mason. **7.6b**, Peter Gould. **7.6c**, Gareth Boden. **7.7a**, Courtesy of Ford Motors. **7.7b**, Robert Harding Picture Library. **7.7c**, Collections/Brian Shuel. **7.7d**, Trevor Hill. **7.8a-d**, Gareth Boden. **8.3a**, Action Plus. **8.3b**, NHPA/Eric Soder. **8.3c-d**, The Stock Market. **8.3e**, Courtesy of Ford Motors. **9.1a**, Oxford Scientific Films/Edwin Sadd. **9.1b**, Zoological Society of London. **9.1c**, Bruce Coleman. **9.1d**, NHPA/A.N.T. **9.1e**, Bruce Coleman. **9.2a**, Sally & Richard Greenhill. **9.2b**, Science Photo Library/Science Pictures. **9.2c**, Science Photo Library/Andy Walker, Midland Fertility Service. **9.3a**, Science Photo Library/D. Phillips. **9.3b**, Science Photo Library/Don Fawcett. **9.3c-d**, Sally & Richard Greenhill. **9.4a**, Science Photo Library/Professors P.M. Motta & S. Makeabe. **9.4b**, Science Photo Library/Petit Format, Nestle. **9.4c**, Science Photo Library/Alex Bartel. **9.4d**, Sally & Richard Greenhill. **9.6a**, Bruce Coleman. **9.6b**, NHPA/A. Warburton & S. Toon.

The publishers have made every effort to trace copyright holders, but if they have inadvertently overlooked any, they will be pleased to make the necessary arrangements at the first opportunity.